EVENING STAR

EVENING STAR

BY

MARTIN EVANS

AND

'L.B.S.C.'

Model & Allied Publications
Argus Books Ltd.

Model and Allied Publications
Argus Books Ltd.
14 St. James Road,
Watford, Herts.
England

© Argus Books Ltd. 1980
© Martin Evans 1980

ISBN 0 85242 634 8

First Published 1980

Typeset by Inforum Ltd, Portsmouth
Thomson Litho Ltd, East Kilbride, Scotland

Contents

Introduction

It was hardly surprising that the late "LBSC" should have chosen the British Railways *Evening Star* 2-10-0 locomotive as the prototype for his 3½ in. gauge version, for this engine was the last steam locomotive to be built for Britain's railways, and a very successful one at that.

No. 92220 was turned out by Swindon Works in 1960, and was the final unit of 999 steam locomotives to British Railways standard designs which had been built since nationalisation of the railways in 1948. By this act, accompanied by appropriate ceremony, was terminated a century and a half of steam traction development in this country since Trevithick's tiny machine trundled its way along its Welsh track.

The basic dimensions of the Class 9, 2-10-0 locomotives were as follows:- Two cylinders 20 in × 28 in. Working pressure 250 p.s.i., boiler barrel 5 ft. 9 in. dia. increasing to 6 ft. 1 in. There were 138 small tubes of 2 in. dia., and 35 superheater flues of 5¼ in. dia., heating surfaces were tubes 1836 sq. ft., firebox 179 sq. ft., total 2015 sq. ft., superheater 535 sq. ft. Grate area was 40.2 sq. ft. Driving & coupled wheels 5 ft. dia.

The cylinders had piston valves 11 in. dia., operated by Walschaerts valve gear. The steam lap of the valves was 1 & 11/16 in., with ¼ in. lead. There was no exhaust clearance, the valves being set line-for-line on the exhaust side. Maximum cut-off in full gear was 78% and the tractive effort at 85% of working pressure amounted to the respectable figure of 39667 lbs.

The British Railways 2-10-0's were primarily intended for fast freight duties, but they did occasionally blossom forth as express passenger engines. It had been thought that their ten-coupled wheels would prevent them from reaching high speeds, yet it was reported that on occasion they could touch 90 m.p.h.! During June 1960, Class 9's worked the "Red Dragon" and "Capitals United" South Wales expresses from Cardiff to Paddington and back, and kept time too, with reported speeds of 80-85 m.p.h., but these exploits did not last long as Officialdom intervened!

For a short time, the 2-10-0's worked over the heavily graded Somerset & Dorset line, taking trains of 400 to 450 tons single-handed, with power outputs of 2000 (equivalent drawbar horsepower).

Several modifications were tried on the 2-10-0's. Most notable of these was the Franco-Crosti boiler, where the products of combustion were first passed through a normal boiler barrel and then backwards through a "Preheater", finally being ejected by an unusual type of chimney on the side of the boiler, the normal chimney being used only for lighting purposes. The other important modification was the fitting of a "Giesl" oblong ejector in place of the normal chimney and blastpipe. This was the invention of an Austrian engineer, Dr. Adolf Giesl-Gieslingen, and in the case of that fitted to Class 9 No. 92250, seven blast nozzles were used, in line, under the oblong-shaped chimney. The idea of this invention was that an increased draught on the fire could be obtained without any increase in back pressure in the exhaust. Alternately, the same draught could be had with reduced back pressure.

In tests with both the Crosti-boilered engines and the Giesl-fitted engine, it was found that there was very little improvement in steaming or fuel economy, compared with a standard double-chimney 2-10-0 in good condition.

The model

LBSC's $3\frac{1}{2}$ in. gauge version of the British Railways 2-10-0 will have the normal double chimney, as fitted to the original *Evening Star*, but an alternative single chimney and blast-pipe will also be described, for those who do not wish to go to the added complication of the double arrangement.

The frames will be made from 1/8 in. mild steel with a somewhat simplified arrangement of staying. Cast hornblocks are used, with solid axleboxes. No oil pipes are required, as the bearings and sliding surfaces can be oiled from the outside. The pony truck can be cast or built up. No side control springs are specified for the sake of simplicity; the friction between the top bar and the bearing plate should be sufficient to prevent "nosing" on a straight line, and yet leave the wheels free to follow a curve at speed without derailment.

The ten coupled wheels are $3\frac{3}{4}$ in. dia., the centre pair having no flanges, as on the full-size locomotive.

The cylinders are gunmetal castings, though there is no reason why builders should not use cast iron if they prefer it. They are $1\frac{1}{4}$ in. bore and $1\frac{3}{4}$ in. stroke, with 11/16 in. piston valves of rustless steel, running in pressed-in gunmetal liners. Alternative slide valve cylinders will also be described, for those who prefer them to piston valves. The valve gear is Walschaerts, the only ticklish parts of which are the brackets which carry the expansion links. Valve spindle guides are not specified, though the more ambitious builders may decide to fit them, as in full-size practice.

On the big engine, the boiler is built up in sections which telescope over one another, giving a bigger diameter at the firebox than at the smokebox, but the barrel of the model may be a single piece of seamless copper tube, brazed to the throatplate of the firebox wrapper, which simplifies construction. The inside of the boiler contains a combustion chamber self-stayed by watertube struts, a great help to circulation, and three large superheater flues, each containing two elements.

The boiler is fed by a pump driven by an eccentric on one of the axles, and also by an injector located on the left-hand side below the cab. Both deliver the feed water through clacks on the top of the barrel, as in full size. An emergency hand pump is also provided, in the tender; inexperienced enginemen will probably find this useful, and of course it can also be used for boiler-testing.

The backhead fittings have been arranged so that they are reasonably accessible to a driver sitting on a flat car behind the tender.

The full-size locomotive has a double chimney with a special copper top, as Swindon practice. While this is not usually the best arrangement for a $3\frac{1}{2}$ in. gauge locomotive, it is rather conspicuous, so it is included, together with double blast pipes and blowers to suit. However, the drawings include an alternative single chimney arrangement, for those who prefer it.

For the smokebox, we can either use steel sheet rolled up, with the joint brazed, or seamless brass tube, which although more expensive, is easier to make. Both smokebox door and ring are castings in gunmetal.

The superstructure — cab, running boards etc — follows full-size practice and is built up mainly from brass sheet, and forms a nice exercise in sheet-metal working. It was a tight squeeze to get in the brake gear owing to the very close spacing of the driving and coupled wheels, especially as we have to use flanges which are rather deeper than the "scale" equivalent. The driving wheels, middle pair, have no flanges, just plain flat treads, to assist the engine on sharp curves.

Beginners may find the tender rather a difficult customer, as it is quite different to the usual type used on British railways; however, if the sheet metal work is taken step by step, in easy stages, it will not seem too bad.

CHAPTER ONE

"LBSC leads off with a description of the frames"

The first job in building any locomotive is to cut out the frame plates, and for these we shall need two pieces of 1/8 in. mild steel, 30 in. long and 3¾ in. wide. Either the bright or blue kind may be used, as long as it is soft and ductile. Hard-rolled material is unsuitable; though it may be flat to start with, it warps and twists as soon as it is cut and drilled. Make sure that each piece is perfectly flat, then mark out one of them as shown in the drawing.

Bright steel should be given a coating of marking-out fluid, easily made by dissolving some shellac in methylated spirit and adding a little blue or violet aniline dye. Most chemists will make up a small quantity. If applied with a soft brush it dries in a few seconds, and scriber marks made on it stand out like railway lines in bright sunshine. Blue steel, if clean, requires no treatment, as the scriber marks usually show up bright.

Make sure that one edge of the plate is perfectly straight, and on this, set out the five openings for the hornblocks. First mark off the centre lines, starting from the front edge of the plate; then on these centre-lines, set out the openings, using a try-square to get them at right-angles to the edge of the frame. The outline of the frame can then be very carefully marked out, checking every measurement as the job proceeds. I very strongly recommend all beginners and inexperienced workers, to obtain a full-sized drawing of the frames, because it is much easier to work from this, rather than to take the measurements from the small drawings in this book. I once had a friend, an engine driver, who used to paste the actual drawing on to the metal and then cut it out. The snag was, that the drawing shrank, so all the measurements came out wrong!

Mark off all the holes shown on the drawing to the given measurements, and make a fairly deep centre "pop" at each location. The exact position of the 3/16 in. diameter hole at the front end of the frame doesn't matter very much, as it only represents the hole in the full-size engine where the crane hook goes in when the engine is lifted. The others should be as shown, unless the builder wishes to braze the frames into the slots in the buffer and drag beams, though I do not recommend this method for inexperienced workers, owing to the danger of distortion.

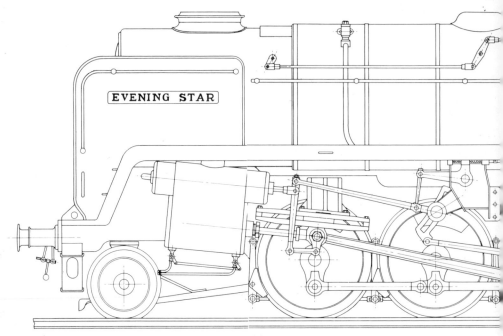

EVENING STAR

$3\frac{1}{2}$ in. gauge version of the last steam locomotive built for British Railways

How to cut out the frames

As the two frame plates must be exactly alike, they are always cut out together. Drill any one of the screw-holes at each end of the marked-out plate, remove any burrs, then temporarily clamp the plates together and drill two holes in the unmarked plate, using those in the marked-out plate as guides. Put a couple of rivets through the holes and burr them over, so that the two plates are held firmly together. Now drill all the other holes right through both plates at once. Countersink those shown in the drawing with a ring round them, using a 7/32 in. or No. 2 drill, on both sides. The countersinks then indicate which is the outside of each frame plate, one right hand and one left hand.

Much of the surplus metal around the outline of the frames can be cut away with a hacksaw. Don't use a blade with less than 22 teeth to the inch, or the job will look as if it had paid a visit to the dentist. Also never use a dry blade to cut steel; lubricate it with the same cutting oil as you use for turning steel in the lathe. Any good cutting oil will do. Some kinds are mixed with water, forming an emulsion like milk, but my favourite is a brand called "Cutmax", to which I add half its bulk of paraffin. Applied with a brush, this enables the saw blade to walk through the steel like nobody's business, and makes the blades last much longer. When used for turning steel in the lathe, it doesn't leave a sticky mess like water-diluted oil, but keeps the machine in new condition.

When sawing along the straight lines, use the top of the vice jaws for a guide wherever possible, setting the marked line level with the jaw tops, and sawing

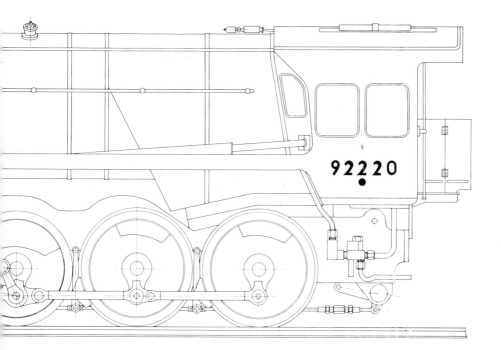

along with the blade resting on them. The blade can be set sideways in the saw frame for this purpose. When cutting the hornblock openings, drill a row of holes, using No. 40 drill, just below the marked line at the top of each opening. Put the frames upside down in the bench vice, with the row of holes just showing above the jaws; saw down to them, keeping just inside the marked lines each side. Grab the metal between the saw cuts with a pair of pliers, and waggle them back and forth like a dentist trying to pull out a troublesome tooth. The metal will break away along the line of holes. Trim the ragged opening to shape and size with a flat file, plus a small round one for the corners, using a gauge to get all the openings "spot on". This could be just a short length of 1 in. × 1/4 in. flat bar, brass or steel, with one end rounded off to the shape of the openings, as shown on the drawing. File the openings until the gauge will just slide in without shake. Finally, trim off any raggedness along the sawn outer edges of the frame, so that it conforms to the drawing; knock out the rivets, part the two plates, smooth off any burring along the edges and around the rivet holes, and stage one is completed.

Buffer and drag beams

The beams can be made from 1 in. × 1/8 in. steel angle or from castings. If angle is used, two pieces are needed, one $5\frac{3}{4}$ in. long, and one 5 in., after the ends have been filed off square. Bright soft angle should be used, though

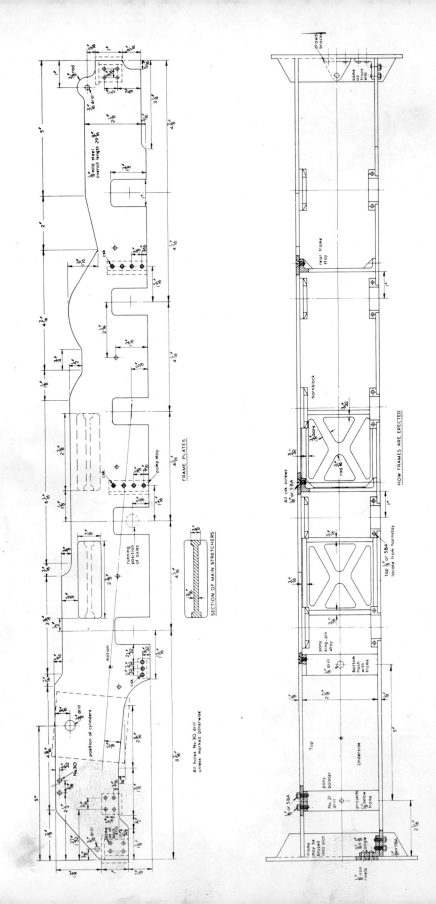

FRAME PLATES

SECTION OF MAIN STRETCHERS

All holes No.30 drill
unless marked otherwise

HOW FRAMES ARE ERECTED

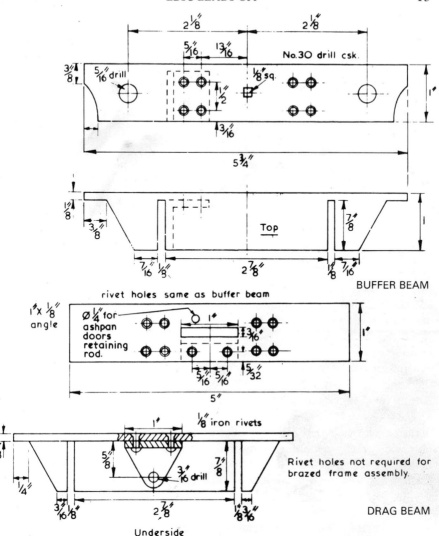

BUFFER BEAM

rivet holes same as buffer beam

DRAG BEAM

Rivet holes not required for brazed frame assembly.

Underside

common black stuff could be used at a pinch. Coat one member of the longer piece with marking-out fluid and carefully mark it out as shown on the drawing. Centre-pop and drill all the holes first with No. 30 drill; then open out the large ones with 5/16 in. drill. Countersink the rivet holes with 7/32 in. or no. 2 drill, and file the middle one square, with a square file, until a piece of 1/8 in. square silver-steel will slide easily into it. The ends are scalloped out with a half-round file, as shown in the drawing. This is done on the full-size engine to give platform clearance.

The other member, which forms the top of the beam, has to be slotted to take the ends of the frame plates—and this is where you want to watch your step; so much depends on true slots. If they aren't true, the frame plates won't be square

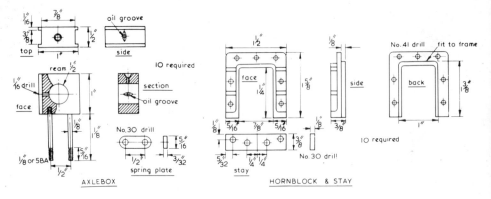

AXLEBOX   HORNBLOCK & STAY

with the beams and when assembled, the whole bag of tricks will assume a rhomboidal shape. If a 1/8 in. saw-type milling cutter is available, large enough in diameter to reach to the bottom of the slots, the job is comparatively easy. Just after the Kaiser's war, I bought one (Government surplus) for a shilling, and mounted it on an arbor made from an old $\frac{1}{2}$ in. bolt. The bolt head was sawn off, and the cutter, which was 3 in. dia., was clamped between two nuts on the screwed part. The beam was clamped under the slide-rest tool-holder, parallel with the centre-line of the lathe, and set with the marked location of the slot exactly opposite the cutter, the improvised arbor being held in the chuck. With the lathe running at slow speed, the beam was fed carefully on to the cutter, cutting oil being applied with a brush. The result was a perfect slot.

The slots can be cut by hand if no cutter is available. Put the beam vertically in the bench vice with the marked edge of the slots level with the top of the vice jaws and saw along the line, using the jaw top to guide the saw blade. Repeat with the other edge of the slot, then clean the ragged edges with a thin flat file, such as a key-cutter's warding file, until a piece of 1/8 in. steel plate will fit tightly. Each end of the top of the beam is sawn to the shape shown in the drawing.

The face of the 5 in. drag beam has eight countersunk rivet holes drilled in it, to the same spacing as those in the face of the buffer beam. In addition there are two more, for the attachment of the bracket which carries the drawbar. The slot for the drawbar is 1 in. long and 3/16 in. wide. Drill a row of 5/32 in. holes along the marked out oblong, then run them into a slot with a "rat-tail" file, finishing off to correct size with a thin flat file. The bracket itself is filed up from a piece of the same kind of steel angle used for the beam, to the shape shown in the drawing. Drill a 3/16 in. dia. hole in the apex of the triangle, as shown, for the drawbar pin. Clamp the bracket to the inner side of the beam, with the triangular part level with the bottom of the drawbar slot. A toolmaker's clamp put over bracket and beam between the rivet holes will hold it firmly. Put the No. 30 drill through the rivet holes in the beam, carrying on right through the bracket; file off any burring and rivet the bracket to the beam with a couple of

1/8 in. iron rivets. Hammer the shanks well into the countersinks and file off flush. Finally put the 3/16 in. drill through the hole in the bracket, and drill a corresponding hole through the beam, using the hole in the bracket as guide, so that the holes line up.

Brackets for attaching frames

Take a look at the drawing of the frame assembly and you will see that the frame plates are jammed tightly into the slots in the tops of the beams, and screwed to pieces of angle which are riveted to the beams. Four pieces of $\frac{3}{4}$ in. × 1/8 in. angle are needed, each 7/8 in. long. To locate them correctly, jam any odd bit of frame steel left over from frame cutting into one of the slots. Set the piece of angle right close to it and clamp it tightly with a toolmaker's clamp. Put a No. 30 drill through two of the holes in the beam, and carry on right through the angle. Remove the clamp, put two 1/8 in. iron rivets in the holes, hammer the shanks well down into the countersinks on the face of the beam, drill the other two holes and repeat the riveting job. File the rivets flush with the face of the beam. Repeat operations with the other three pieces of angle, attaching them to the beams flush with the inner edges of the slots.

Note. If cast beams are used, lugs for attachment of the frame plates will be integral with the casting, and there will be no need to fit the pieces of angle as described above. The only job will be to cut the four slots in which the frame plates are fitted, and this is done in exactly the same manner as those in beams made from angle. The bracket for supporting the drawbar will also be cast on, and will only need drilling for the drawbar pin.

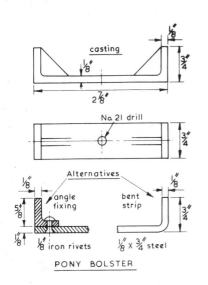

PONY BOLSTER

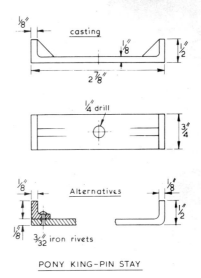

PONY KING-PIN STAY

How to erect the frames

Erection of the frames is a very important job; everything depends on it. If the frame assembly is out of true, the whole engine will be affected. The frame plates and beams must form a true rectangle. Like every other job, it is easy when you know how. All I use are four small clamps, a try square and the lathe bed, and this is how the trick is done. First push the ends of the frame plates into the slots in the beam, as shown on the plan drawing, setting the lot square as near as you can by eye. Next, stand the assembly on the lathe bed, right way up, with the bottom edges—where the hornblock openings are—resting on the bed. The tailstock will probably have to be taken off for this job, and the saddle run up as close to the headstock as possible, to make enough room.

Adjust the frames until they sit on the lathe bed without shake, both frames resting on the bed for their full length. Next, set the buffer beam so that the bottom edge of it is exactly 7/8 in. above the bed, for the full width of the beam. For a gauge, I use a piece of steel bar of correct width; but both ends of the beam can be checked by inside calipers, or by a scribing-block, otherwise known as a surface gauge, or even by measuring from bed to beam with a steel rule. Now put a clamp tightly over the frame and piece of angle on the beam, at each end. Turn the frame end-for-end on the lathe bed, and repeat operations on the drag beam. See that all the clamps are tight, then apply the try-square to beam and frame at each end. You will see at a glance whether the frames and beams are square with each other; if not, adjust until they are. Then, with the frames touching the bed for full contact length, and the bottom of the beams exactly 7/8 in. above it for full width, the assembly is "spot on."

The clamps shouldn't be applied so that they cover all four holes at each end of the frame; they will hold tight enough if two holes at each end are left open. Run a No. 30 drill into each hole, and make countersinks with it on the pieces of angle attached to the beams. Follow through with No. 40 drill, going right through the angles. Tap 5 BA, and put temporary screws in. When all four corners are done, remove clamps and repeat the countersinking, drilling and tapping through the holes previously covered by the clamps. There is no need to put screws in these yet, as the frames have to be taken apart again to fit the hornblocks; but put the frame assembly, held by the temporary screws, on the lathe bed again, and recheck to make sure that nothing has shifted during the drilling and tapping process. Should the frames rock slightly on the bed, or the beams be slightly out of line, slacken the screws slightly, set the assembly true again, and then re-tighten the screws.

The Hornblocks

Ten hornblocks are required, and these may be either of the hot-pressed alloy kind, or ordinary bronze or iron castings. Although the former are slightly less resistant to wear than cast hornblocks, they save quite a lot of machining, as they usually fit the openings in the frame without any attention at all. At most, a slight cleaning with a file on the contact side which goes next to the frame plate, will enable the flange to fit nicely in the opening. Drill seven No. 41 holes in each; fit each to an opening, making sure that it beds tightly against the frame plate. Clamp temporarily in place, then run the No. 41 drill through the frame, using the holes in the hornblock as guides. Countersink these holes on the outside of the frame, and rivet up with 3/32 in. charcoal-iron rivets. Hammer the shanks well down into the countersinks, and file off flush. There must be no projection outside the frame. Tip: to support the rivets while hammering, drill a countersink the size of the rivet head, in the end of a short piece of $\frac{1}{2}$ in $\times$ $\frac{1}{4}$ in. steel rod, close to the edge. Hold this vertically in the bench vice, and rest the rivet head in the countersink while wielding the hammer.

The cast hornblocks, if reasonably clean, may only need a little filing on the backs, to enable them to fit the openings. Should the castings be rough, it is easy enough to machine them up accurately in the lathe, by aid of a vertical slide. First smooth off the flange on the ribbed side of the hornblock by rubbing it on a big flat file laid on the bench, or on a piece of coarse emery-cloth laid on the lathe bed, or something equally flat and true. Bolt it to the vertical slide, back outwards, by a bolt in one of the tee-slots, with a square washer about 1/8 in. thick under the unit. The washer mustn't exceed the width over flange at each side. Set the hornblock vertically by aid of a try-square, then set the vertical slide at right angles to the lathe centres: easily done by putting the faceplate on the mandrel nose, and setting the face of the vertical slide parallel to it. Put an endmill, or home-made slot drill, in the three-jaw chuck, then manipulate the slide handles until the part of the back of the hornblock to be machined is opposite the cutter. Feed the hornblock on to the cutter by moving the saddle; then the two sides of the hornblock back can be faced off by moving the vertical slide up and down, and the top piece by moving the cross-slide. The cutter shouldn't be less than 3/8 in. dia.

When all the hornblocks are riveted on, bolt the frames back to back with the hornblocks outwards. Be careful to line them up exactly. The jaws can then be machined out to take the axleboxes, by bolting a machine-vice to the vertical

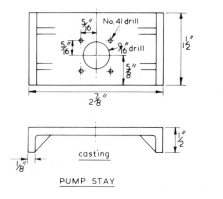

PUMP STAY

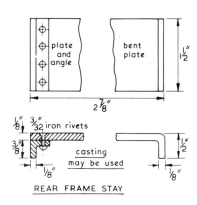

REAR FRAME STAY

slide, holding the frames in it, with the jaws to be machined centrally with the vice jaws, and moving the hornblock up and down over the side of an endmill, about 5/8 in. dia. held in the chuck. The jaws can also be smoothed out by hand; grip the frames in the bench vice with one pair of hornblocks central with the vice jaws, and file out the hornblock jaws until a piece of bar 7/8 in. wide, slides easily between them without shake. Finally, smooth off all the hornblock feet flush with the bottom edges of the frames, which may now be re-erected "for keeps."

Axleboxes

The axleboxes can be made from 1 in $\times \frac{1}{2}$ in. hard drawn bronze or gunmetal bar, or from castings. Advertisers usually supply the lot cast in one stick. Saw or part off from the bar, five pieces each sufficient for two axleboxes. First job is to mill the grooves to fit the hornblock jaws. If a regular milling-machine is available, just grip each piece in a machine-vice on the table, setting it level by applying the needle of a scribing-block to each end. Traverse it under a 3/8 in. side-and-face cutter on the arbor, taking a cut 1/16 in. deep. Reverse, and ditto-repeato. For the second cut I always put a piece of bar between the vice runners and the groove, which ensures them being parallel, and carefully check the width of the box between bottoms of grooves with a slide-gauge.

To do the job in the lathe, grip the piece of bar under the slide-rest toolholder. Pack it up so that the centre of the bar is dead level with lathe centres. Set it at right angles to the bed, by putting on the faceplate and holding a steel rule, or a parallel piece of bar, between faceplate and axlebox blank. Put a 3/8 in. endmill or slotdrill in the three-jaw, and feed the blank on to it by turning the handle of the top slide. Traverse the blank right across the cutter, and there is your groove. Turn the blank over and repeat operation. Check width over grooves, either with a slide-gauge set to 7/8 in. or by cutting an opening 7/8 in. wide and $1\frac{1}{4}$ in. deep (same as the hornblock jaws) in a piece of sheet metal about 3/32 in. thick, and using it for a gauge. It should slide easily in the grooves.

Fitting Axleboxes and Hornblocks

Saw each of the pieces of grooved bar in half, then face off the ends in the four-jaw chuck until each is exactly 1 in. long. Fit each to a hornblock, in which it should slide freely without shake. Mark the hornblocks and axleboxes 1 to 5 on one frame, and 6 to 10 on the other, so that once fitted, they can always be replaced in their proper order. Find the exact centre of axleboxes 1 to 5, centrepop them deeply, and drill a No. 30 hole in each. Either use a drilling machine, or drill them in the lathe, with the drill in the three-jaw and the axlebox held up tightly against a drilling-pad in the tailstock barrel. Don't drill by hand on any account, as the holes must go through dead square. Next clamp box No. 1 to box No. 6 exactly in line; I always use a piece of grooved bar at

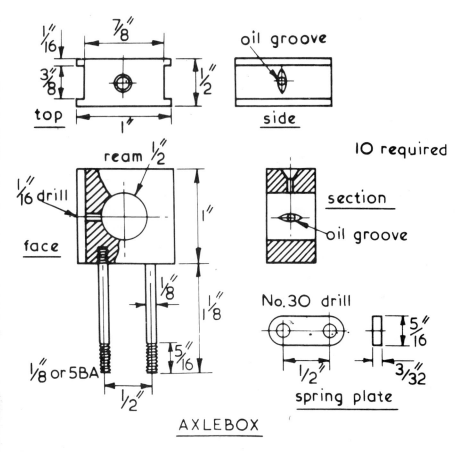

AXLEBOX

each side. Then drill No. 6, using the hole in No. 1 as guide, and repeat operation with No. 2 and 7, 3 and 8, 4 and 9, and 5 and 10. This little wheeze ensures that if any slight error is made in drilling the axleboxes on one side of the frame, and it is easily done, the box on the opposite side will have a similar error, and the axles will still be at right angles to the frame, which is all that matters.

Put all the axleboxes back in the hornblocks, and check for truth by putting a piece of 1/8 in. silver-steel through each pair. This should lie exactly at right angles to the frames. If it doesn't, correct the holes with a rat-tail file, clamp the boxes together again, and put a 3/16 in. drill through them. Recheck with a piece of 3/16 in. silver-steel. This kind is usually straight enough to use for checking. The boxes should now be O.K. and the holes may be opened out with 31/64 in. drill, and reamed ½ in. The oil holes may then be drilled. The top one is drilled 1/16 in. and countersunk. The side holes are also drilled 1/16 in. and a slight groove is made inside the axle hole. This can be done with a little chisel made from 3/32 in. silver-steel. File the end off on the slant, heat the end to red, plunge into cold water, rub the filed part on an oilstone until it is bright and smooth, then lay the chisel on a piece of sheet iron about 1/16 in. thick, and hold it over a gas or spirit flame. As soon as the bright part turns dark yellow, tip the chisel into the cold water. It is then ready for use. Make a similar nick at each side of the box, where the oil hole comes out into the groove, as shown.

If the axleboxes are made from cast bar, each sawn-off length should be chucked in the four-jaw and faced off front and back, to bring the thickness to $\frac{1}{2}$ in. before carrying out the above operation.

Hornstays and Spring Pins

The hornstays are made from 1/8 in. × 3/8 in. mild steel strip, ten pieces each $1\frac{1}{2}$ in. long being required. Mark one off as shown in the drawing, being careful to get the two middle holes on the centre-line. Centre-pop deeply, and drill No. 30. File off any burring, then use the drilled hornstay as a jig to drill the other nine. Be sure that the drilled one and the blank are clamped together in line, so that all holes are exactly the same. Next clamp each to the bottom of a hornblock, with the offset holes against the centres of the lugs or feet. Run the No. 30 drill through the holes, making countersinks on the lugs; follow through with No. 40 drill, and tap 5 B.A. Remove hornstays, put the axleboxes in, and replace hornstays, fixing with screws as shown.

Jam each axlebox tightly against the hornstay by putting a wooden wedge between the box and the end of the hornblock jaws. Run the No. 30 drill through the middle holes in the stay, making countersinks on the bottom of the box. Drill the countersinks about $\frac{1}{4}$ in. deep with No. 40 drill, and tap 5 B.A. I usually jam up all the boxes, put the frame assembly upside down on the drilling-machine table, make the countersinks with a No. 30 drill in the chuck, then change the drill for a No. 40 and drill the boxes through the holes in the hornstays. Then I shift the assembly to the bench, and tap the holes through the hornstays, which ensures the tapped holes being accurate. It's quick, too! If a drilling machine isn't available, drill the holes in the lathe, with a No. 40 drill in the chuck, and the box held against the tailstock drilling-pad. When tapping, be sure to put the tap in quite square with the end of the box.

For the spring pins you'll need twenty 1.5/16 in. lengths of 1/8 in. round silver-steel. One end of each is screwed for 5/16 in. length, and the other for 3/16 in. length, all 5 B.A. Grip each tightly in the three-jaw, and use a die held in a tailstock die-holder. Pull the lathe belt by hand while feeding the die on to the pin, and use plenty of cutting oil, to make certain of clean threads.

Spring Plates

The spring plates are made from 5/16 in × 3/32 in. mild steel strip, in exactly the same way as the hornstays, drilling one and using it as a jig to drill the others. The whole lot can then be assembled using ordinary commercial steel nuts under the plates. To wind the springs, put a piece of 1/8 in. round steel in the chuck, poke the end of the 19g. spring wire between two of the jaws, pull the lathe belt by hand, and guide the wire on to the rod with your thumb. It doesn't hurt! Wind on enough for about four springs at each go. Snip off the lengths with cutting pliers, then touch each end of the spring on a fast-running emery-wheel to square it off.

Bolster and Stays

The pony bolster and king-pin stay, pump and rear stays may be cast or built up. If cast, the ends may be milled, if a machine is available, by holding in a machine-vice on a table, and running under a cutter about 1 in. wide on the arbor. They can be milled in the lathe by holding in a machine-vice bolted to the vertical slide, and traversing across an endmill held in the chuck. Failing that, they can be done by hand. Grip in a bench vice, with the end just showing above the tops of the jaws, and go to work with a big flat second-cut file. Take it steady, and be sure to hold the file level. Check with a try-square, and finish exactly to width shown, viz. 2.7/8 in.

To build up, either use pieces of 1/8 in. steel plate (same as used for frames) with pieces of brass angle riveted along each side as shown, or cut the pieces of steel to 2.7/8 in. plus twice the depth of flange, and bend the ends over to form the flanges. This is easy if a bending machine is available, but I don't recommend it otherwise. Drill the holes as shown, then put each in place between the frames in the positions shown in the frame assembly drawing. Put a big clamp over the frames to prevent shifting, run the No. 30 drill through the holes in frames, making countersinks on the flanges, follow through with No. 40, tap 5 B.A. and fix with countersunk screws.

A three-quarter rear view of a full-size "Evening Star". B.R. No. 92159

Another example of the British Railways 2-10-0   B.R. No. 92167

CHAPTER TWO

The Wheels

Now we can make a start on the wheels. Grip each wheel casting by the tread in the three-jaw, setting it to run truly. Centre it with a big centre-drill in the tailstock chuck. First put a $\frac{1}{4}$ in. drill through to make a pilot hole, then follow with a 27/64 in. drill, and finally a 7/16 in. reamer. Face off the back with a round-nose tool set crosswise in the rest, and take a slight cut off the flange, to true it up. Don't forget that a slow speed is necessary to turn cast-iron. If you go too fast the tool's edge will be finished in a few seconds. The boss is turned flush with the rim.

Reverse in chuck and grip by the flange. Face off the rim to 7/16 in. thickness, then face the boss until it stands 1/16 in. proud of the rim. Change the round-nose tool for a parting tool, and cut a little rebate (small shoulder) at the point where the spokes join the rim. This represents the joint between wheel centre and tyre in a full-size wheel.

Treads and flanges are finished with the wheel mounted on an improvised faceplate. For this I use an old wheel casting a little smaller than the wheel to be turned; any piece of similar size will do. Chuck in three-jaw, face-off, and recess the centre about 1/32 in. depth for about 1 in. dia. Centre, drill a $\frac{1}{4}$ in. pilot hole,

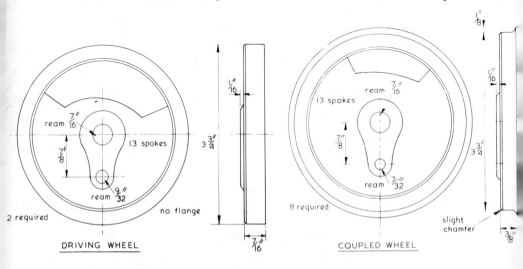

open out to 15/32 in. and tap any fine thread, $\frac{1}{2}$ in. dia. Put $\frac{1}{2}$ in. of similar thread on the end of a piece of $\frac{1}{2}$ in. round mild steel about $1.\frac{1}{2}$ in. long. Screw this tightly into the hole, and turn the projecting part until the wheels will just slide on without shake. Screw about $\frac{1}{2}$ in. of the end with a 7/16 in. die in the tailstock holder, and fit a nut to suit.

Mount each wheel on to the stub, face outward, and secure it with the nut, but don't tighten the nut enough to distort the wheel. Then with a roundnose tool, turn tread and flange to within a few thousandths of an inch of finished size. When the last one is done, regrind the tool and take the final cut to bring it to size; then mount each wheel on the stub and take the final cut without shifting the cross-slide. Each wheel will then be exactly the same diameter without further need of measurement. Before removing, hold a file to each flange, to round it off while still revolving; then hold the file to the edge of the tread, to chamfer it slightly, as shown. Don't forget that the driving wheels—those with the big balance-weights—have plain flat treads with no flanges.

Drilling Jig

It is absolutely essential that the holes for the crankpins are exactly the same distance from the axle holes, so a drilling jig for the crankpin holes in the wheel bosses is made from a $1.\frac{1}{2}$ in. length of 1 in. × $\frac{1}{4}$ in. steel bar. Scribe a line down the middle, and make two deep centrepops on it 7/8 in. apart. Drill through with 13/64 in. drill, using either drilling-machine or lathe; the holes must go through dead square, or the jig will be useless. Open out one hole with a 27/64in. drill. Chuck a piece of $\frac{1}{2}$ in. round mild steel in the three-jaw, face the end, and turn 1 in. length to a sliding fit, without shake (very important, that) in the axle hole in the wheel.

Further reduce 3/8 in. length to a press fit in the larger hole in the jig. For beginners' benefit, here is a simple way of turning press fits. First turn the metal to a shade larger diameter than the hole, then turn 1/8 in. of the end so that it will just enter the hole tightly. Note the position of the graduated collar behind the cross-slide handle. Myford and similar lathes all have them, but if there isn't one, note position of the handle itself. Move the handle back half-turn, then bring it forward again until within half a division of its previous position. This neutralises any slackness between the cross-slide screw and nut. Take the finishing cut over the rest of the 3/8 in. length with that setting, and it will be a press fit in the hole in the jig. If the cross-slide handle had no graduated collar, bring the handle back a little short of its original position, using your own judgment.

Part off the turned piece of rod at $\frac{1}{2}$ in. from the shoulder, and squeeze it into the hole in the jig, using the bench vice as a screw-press. To use the jig, insert the peg in the axle hole in the wheel boss, and adjust the jig until the small hole is central. Clamp the jig to the wheel boss, and drill the boss 13/64 in. using the

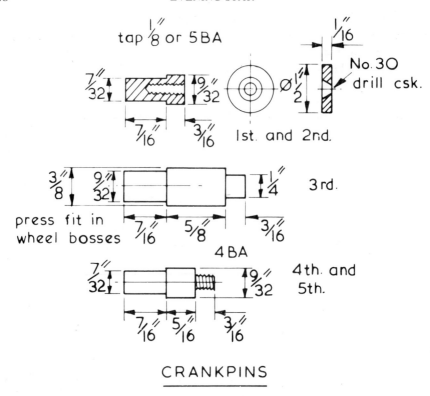

CRANKPINS

hole in the jig to guide the drill. After drilling all ten, put a 7/32 in. parallel reamer through all the holes in the flanged wheels. Those in the driving wheels (flat treads) are opened out with a 17/64 in. drill and reamed 9/32 in. Bigger crankpins are needed to take the driving stresses.

Crankpins

The crankpins are made from silver-steel, the natural polished surface of which is resistant to wear. If the lathe has collets, or if the three-jaw chuck is reasonably true, the steel rod can be gripped direct and turned to the sizes shown on the drawing. If the chuck doesn't hold truly, use a split bush. To make it, chuck a piece of ½ in. brass rod about ¾ in. long. Face the end, centre, drill through 17/64 in. and ream 9/32 in. Make a centrepop on it, opposite No. 1 chuck jaw. Remove from chuck, slit lengthwise with a hacksaw, and replace with the pop mark opposite same jaw. Insert steel to be turned in the bush, tighten the chuck, and go ahead with the turning. The rod will run quite truly. Turn each shank to a press fit in the wheel boss, by the method just described, and part off to the overall length of the pin. Use plenty of cutting oil applied with a brush.

To adapt the split bush for holding the 3/8 in. steel, grip it in the chuck (not tightly enough to close the sawcut) with the pop mark still opposite No. 1 jaw, and bore it out with a little boring tool made from the tang end of a worn-out file until the 3/8 in. steel will just slide in. Then tighten chuck, and turn the pins to sizes shown.

Grip each short pin in the chuck, holding by the shank. Centre, drill No. 40 to 3/8 in. depth, and tap 1/8 in. or 5 B.A. To tap truly, put the tapwrench tightly on the tap close to the thread, and hold the shank in the tailstock chuck just loosely enough to allow it to slide without shake. Pull the lathe belt by hand, working it up and down, and feed the tap into the hole very carefully by aid of the tapwrench, using plenty of cutting oil. Take the job easy, as silver-steel is mighty hard and tough, and patience is required to get a clean thread.

Turn the outer ends of the longer 9/32 in. pins to 9/64 in. dia. for 3/16 in. length, and screw 4 B.A. with a die in the tailstock holder. The ends of the 3/8 in. pins are turned to $\frac{1}{4}$ in. dia. for 3/16 in. length, and left plain. Finally, press all the shanks into the holes in the wheel bosses, using the bench vice as press, as previously mentioned. To prevent damaging the screwed ends, put a brass nut on while pressing.

Axles

The axles are turned from $\frac{1}{2}$ in. round ground mild steel. Saw or part off five 4.3/8 in. lengths, chuck in the three-jaw and face off each end until the overall length is exactly 4.9/32 in. If the chuck is reasonably true, the axles can be held in it for turning the wheel seats. If it isn't, either make a split bush as described for holding the crankpins truly, or else put a piece of thin metal, such as brass foil or shim steel between the offending jaw and the axle. Turn all the ends for $\frac{1}{2}$ in. length, to approximately 7/16 in. dia., a press fit in the holes in the wheel bosses, by the method previously described.

Next job is drilling the oil ducts. At $\frac{1}{4}$ in. from the shoulder of the wheel seat, turn a groove about 1/16 in. wide and 1/32 in. deep, with a pointed tool rounded off slightly at the end. From the bottom of this groove, drill a 1/16 in.

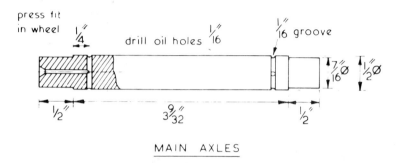

MAIN AXLES

hole right through the axle, so that it emerges in the groove at the opposite side. Chuck the axle in three-jaw, and with a size E centre-drill in the tailstock chuck, make a centre-hole just deep enough to leave a slight countersink at the edge. From the bottom of this, run a 1/16 in. drill into the cross-hole, taking care as the drill breaks through, to avoid breaking off the point.

When the engine is working all you have to do to oil the journals and horn slides, is to apply a small syringe filled with fairly thick oil, or ball-bearing grease, to the centre-hole in the end of the axle, and press the plunger. The oil or grease is then forced through the ducts, and not only provides the necessary lubrication, but forces out any grit that may have found its way in. This system does away with any need for oil cups or boxes with pipes leading to the axleboxes and is far more effective. Incidentally, in the heyday of steam, many full-size American and Continental locomotives had pressure-applied grease lubrication for many of the moving parts. This saved the driver's oil feeder a lot of work!

Eccentrics

Two eccentrics are needed, one for driving the boiler feed pump and one for driving the ratchet gear of the lubricator. I make mine from offcuts of mild steel shafting, which is lovely stuff to turn. For the larger one, chuck a piece of $1\frac{1}{2}$ in. dia. round steel in three-jaw, and face the end. With a parting tool a little over 1/8 in. wide, and the end ground off square, form a groove 3/32 in. deep and $\frac{1}{4}$ in. wide, at 1/16 in. from the edge. Beginner's note: chattering of the tool can be avoided by running the lathe at slow speed, and using plenty of cutting oil. The cutting should come off the steel like a close-coiled watch spring, with a sound like frying bacon, though it doesn't smell so good! Take two cuts to get

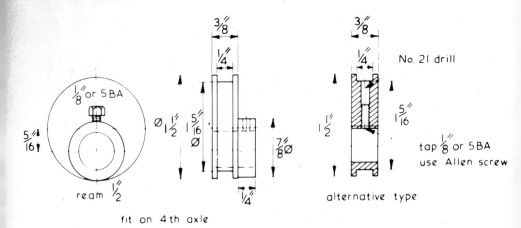

PUMP ECCENTRIC

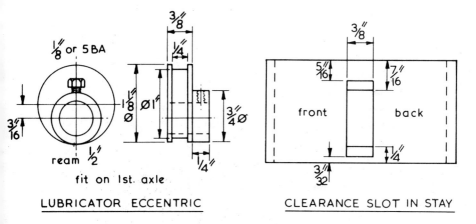

LUBRICATOR ECCENTRIC   CLEARANCE SLOT IN STAY

the required width of groove, and work the tool from side to side at the bottom of the groove, to get a smooth finish. Part off at 5/8 in. from the end.

The facing tool-marks will indicate the true centre. At 5/16 in. from this, make a heavy centrepop, and chuck the piece in the four-jaw independent chuck with the pop mark running truly. Another beginner's tip: bring up the lathe tailstock with its centre-point in the barrel, and you'll see in half-a-tick which chuck jaws need adjusting, and how much, to bring the pop mark "spot-on" to the centre-point. Replace the centre with the tailstock chuck, open the pop mark with a centre-drill run a 31/64 in. drill right through, and follow with a $\frac{1}{2}$ in. parallel reamer. Feed this in slowly, using plenty of cutting oil.

Chuck a short piece of round steel about 5/8 in. dia. and turn 5/8 in. length to a press fit in the $\frac{1}{2}$ in. hole. Press it in from the grooved end of the eccentric, put the rod in the chuck, and turn down the other end of eccentric, to 7/8 in. dia. for

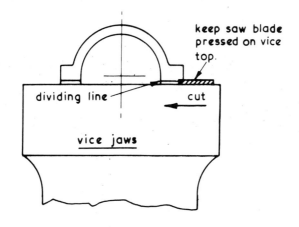

HOW TO DIVIDE STRAP CASTING TRULY

$\frac{1}{4}$ in. length. Be careful when starting the cut, as the steel will be running what the kiddies call "all wobbly". Finally knock out the stub mandrel, drill a No. 40 hole in the boss as shown, and tap it for a setscrew. The eccentric for the lubricator drive is turned in exactly the same way, but from 1.1/8 in. round steel, to the dimensions given in the drawings.

An alternative arrangement is to leave out the boss, making the eccentrics 3/8 in. wide only, and drilling a No. 40 hole from the bottom of the groove, through the widest part of the eccentric, into the $\frac{1}{2}$ in. hole. Open this out with No. 21 drill to half its depth, tap the remainder 5 B.A., and fit an Allen grub screw. Also, iron castings may be used instead of mild steel. These are machined in the same way, being held in the chuck for turning grooves and flanges, by a chucking-piece cast on the side opposite to the boss. This is parted off after the turning is finished.

CHAPTER THREE

Coupling rods

Each coupling-rod is made up of four sections connected by fork-and-tongue knuckle joints, to provide sufficient flexibility to allow the wheels to follow an uneven line. This is more necessary on a small line than a full-size one, as the "'umps and 'ollers" are far greater in proportion.

Four pieces of 7/8 in. × $\frac{1}{4}$ in. mild steel bar are needed for the end sections, each 4.1/8 in. long; two 5.7/8 in. lengths for the driving sections, and two 4.3/8 in. for the intermediates. Coat the pieces which will form one complete rod with marking-out fluid, mark them off as shown, and drill a No. 31 hole at each end, through the pin or bush holes. These holes must go through dead square. File off any burring, clamp each section to its "opposite mate"—line them up carefully—and drill the latter, using the holes in the marked sections as guides. Drive in bits of 1/8 in. steel to keep the pieces together, and file these flush, so that the sections can be held in either bench or machine vice.

If a regular milling machine is available, the surplus metal top and bottom can be removed by setting the pair of blanks level in a machine-vice on the table, and running them under a cutter on the arbor; but the wasp in the jampot is that the small radius at each end of the cut, precludes the use of an ordinary cutter. I get over that by using a special endmill (Govt. surplus) 3 in. long and 3/8 in. dia. used as a slabbing cutter, with its shank in the mandrel socket, and its outer end supported by a centre-point in the overhanging arm of the machine. Lubricated from a drip-can on the arm, the way it mows off the unwanted steel is just nobody's business. This antic can be imitated by using an ordinary 3/8 in. endmill, cutting with its side teeth.

There are two ways of doing the job in the lathe. Bolt a long angle-plate to the vertical slide, set it level, and clamp the pair of blanks to it. Put a 3/8 in. endmill in the chuck, and adjust the lathe saddle until the blanks are directly under it. Feed into cut by moving the vertical slide upwards, at the start of cut which is nearest to the operator, and traverse the cross-slide slowly towards you, using plenty of cutting oil.

Way No. 2 is to use the lathe as a regular milling-machine, but the unfortunate thing about modern small lathes is that the saddle has no height adjustment. However, where there's a will there's a way! File a gap 3/8 in. wide at the end of the pair of blanks, to the full depth of the required cut. Bolt a machine-vice to the cross-slide, and set the blanks horizontally in it, at a height that will allow a 3/8 in. endmill in the chuck, to lie 1/8 in. down in the gap. This will allow a cut of that depth to be taken right along the blanks, by traversing the cross slide. Return to starting-point, set the blanks 1/8 in. higher up, take another cut, and ditto-repeato until the surplus metal is all removed. After doing the top and bottoms, the faces of the blanks can be recessed 1/16 in. by the same methods, on the outsides; and this will automatically give you the right-hand and left-hand rods. The left-hand one is shown in the drawing of the assembled rod.

The job can also be done by hand, but it is rather laborious! Grip the blanks in the bench vice with the line of cut just level with the jaw tops. File a gap at one end, just wide enough to take a hacksaw blade on its side. Put a coarse-tooth blade, say about 14 per inch, sideways in the hacksaw frame, rest it in the gap, and saw along the line, letting the jaw tops guide the saw. Cutting oil applied to the blade is a great help. File away the saw marks with a flat file, and finish the radius at each end with a round one. The faces of the rods can be recessed by filing only, as there isn't much metal to remove, and a big flat coarse-toothed file will soon do the trick. Finish with a fine one.

To round off the ends, knock out the pins and part the sections. Chuck a piece of $\frac{1}{2}$ in. square steel rod truly in the four-jaw, and turn a pip on the end about $\frac{1}{4}$ in. long, to a diameter that will fit nicely in the end holes in the blanks, without shake. Set this crosswise under the slide-rest tool holder. Put the end of a rod over the pip, and run it up to 3/8 in. endmill held in the chuck. Hold the outer end as tightly as you can, then feed carefully into cut, and swing the end of the rod slowly round, so that the cutter removes the surplus metal and leaves the end of the rod nicely rounded. By careful to avoid swinging the rod too far, or the cutter will take off the projections which form the oil boxes. The irregular parts of the bosses can be finished off with a file.

To slot the forked ends, clamp each rod under the slide-rest tool-holder at right angles to lathe centres. Put the cutter used for slotting the buffer and drag beams in the chuck, and feed the rod on to it in the same way, running at slow speed and using plenty of cutting oil. The tongues are formed with a pin-drill, 3/8 in. dia. for the outer joints, and $\frac{1}{2}$ in. for the middle one. Pin-drill away 1/16 in. of the boss on each side, so that a 1/8 in. tongue is left in the middle. When the surplus metal around the recess left by the pin-drill has been filed away, the tongue should be a nice fit, without side-shake, in the fork of the adjoining section of rod.

Assembly

The holes in the 3/8 in. forks and tongues can be opened out with a No. 21 drill. Those in the $\frac{1}{2}$ in. ditto can either be drilled 3/16 in. or drilled No. 14 and reamed 3/16 in. putting the tongue in place in the fork, and poking the reamer through the lot, as I usually do. Countersink all the holes in the forks on the

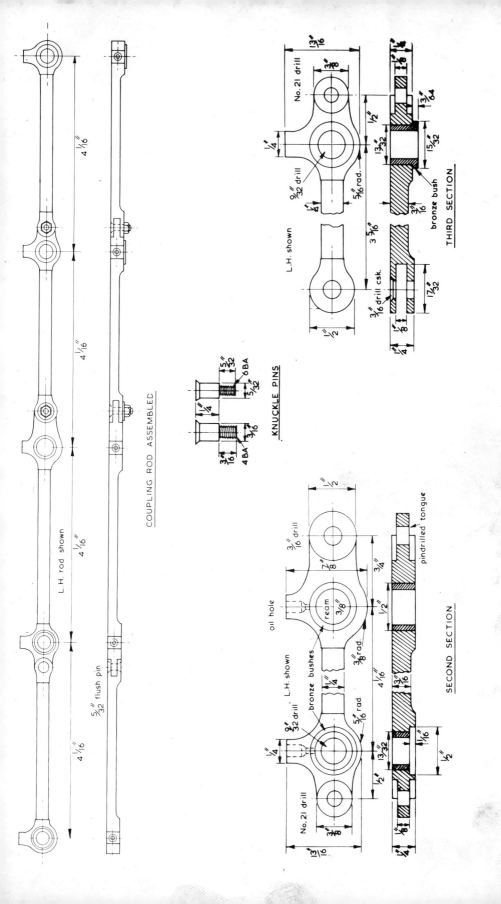

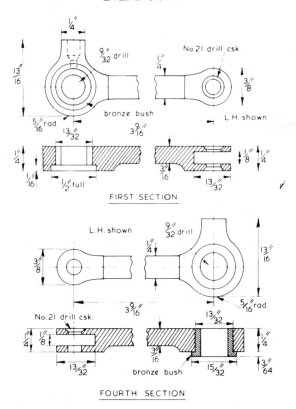

FIRST SECTION

FOURTH SECTION

plain side of the rods, and on the recessed side of the front sections as well. The holes in the bosses are drilled out to the sizes shown in the drawings. Those in the front sections of the rods, and the leading ends of the driving sections, are also pindrilled to 1/16 in. full depth, to the given dimensions, so that the retaining washers will lie flush.

If you want the engine to run perfectly for a long time without undue wear, don't use anything softer than best-grade phosphor-bronze for the bushes. The Stroudley engines on the L.B. & S.C.R. had p-b bushes which ran trouble-free, and showed little wear after years of service.

Turning them is a simple job; the first and second can be turned from 7/16 in. rod held in the chuck. Face off, centre, drill 9/32 in. to $\frac{1}{4}$ in. depth, then turn $\frac{1}{4}$ in. of the outside to a press fit in the hole in the boss. Part off at 3/16 in. from the end. When pressed in, the bushes should be flush with the bottom of the recess. The driving bushes are turned from 9/16 rod. Face, centre, drill 23/64 in. for 5/16 in. depth, turn 5/16 length to a press fit in the big boss, and part off at a full $\frac{1}{4}$ in. from the end. After pressing in, put a 3/8 in. parallel reamer through. The driving bushes should be a nice running fit on the pins, but all the others must be easy, to allow the wheels to "follow the road," as in full-size practice.

At the Southern works at Eastleigh, the bushes in the coupling-rods of all wheels except driving wheels, were bored 1/16 in. bigger than the diameter of the pins, to allow for the up-and-down movement of the wheels when running through crossing-frogs and other rail gaps. This was the cause of the ringing rattle frequently heard when the engines were coasting with steam off. Without the extra play, the rods would bend or break. This was found out by experience in the early days of railways and experience is the best of teachers!

The bushes in the fourth and fifth bosses are flanged. Chuck a piece of $\frac{1}{2}$ in. rod, face, centre, and drill 9/32 in. for 3/8 in. depth. Turn 3/8 in. of the outside to 15/32 in. dia. and further reduce $\frac{1}{4}$ in. of the end, to a press fit on the boss. Part off at bare 1/16 in. from the shoulder, and press in from the recessed side of the rod. Drill a 1/16 in. hole in the projection at the top of each boss right through into the hole in the bush, and counterbore it with a No. 30 drill as shown by dotted lines in the drawing.

Mild steel will do quite well for the knuckle pins, as very little wear takes place here. They can be turned from 5/16 in. round rod held in the chuck. Use a pointed tool with the cutting edge ground off to the same angle as the countersink, and slightly round off the point so that it gives a smooth finish without scratching. Turn the ends with a knife tool, and screw them with a die in the tailstock holder. The parallel part should be a nice push fit, without shake, in the forks and tongues; use plenty of cutting oil for both turning and screwing. The distance from the top of the head to the shoulder should be $\frac{1}{4}$ in. full, so that when the nuts are screwed up tightly the jaws of the fork won't grip the tongue and prevent free movement. This is very important. Ordinary commercial nuts and washers can be used.

The pin in the front knuckle joint isn't screwed as there must be no projection beyond the boss where the connecting-rod passes it. Put a 3/8 in. length of 5/32 in. round rod through the fork and tongue and hammer the projections carefully into the countersinks, but not tightly enough to make the joint stiff. File flush each side.

Quartering the Wheels

The crankpins on one side of the engine are set at right angles to those on the other—known as "quartering" in the railway shops—and those on the right-hand side should lead. That is, when they are on front centre, nearest to the front of the engine, those on the left side should be at the highest point of revolution, or top centre. All you require are a scribing-block or surface gauge, a try-square, and a "straight eye."

The driving wheel on one side should be already pressed on the axle, as mentioned previously. Push the axle through the axleboxes, and put the other driving wheel on the axle as far as it will go without pressing, setting the crankpins as near to right angles as you can get them "by eye." Take out the hornstay screws, lift out the whole assembly, and stand it on something dead flat and true. I use a surface plate, but the lathe bed or the saddle would do. Put a short piece of 1/16 in. silver-steel, or a drill shank (anything straight will do) in the oil duct, letting it project so that its end is level with the end of the crankpin. Fix up the wheels so that they can't roll; a block of wood or metal at each side would do the trick, or you could rest the axle in the groove of a vee-block.

Now set the pressed-on wheel with its crank on bottom centre. Test with the try-square as shown; the edge of the blade should pass exactly across the middle of the crank-pin and the bit of steel in the oil duct. Set the needle of the scribing-block to the centre of the axle, tighten the screws so that the needle can't accidently shift, then apply it to the other crankpin, adjusting the wheel on the axle to bring the centre of the crankpin to coincide with the point of the needle. That is all there is to it.

Inspector Meticulous would probably tell you to set the other four pairs of wheels in the same way, but I know a trick worth two of that. I just push the axles through their respective boxes from the right-hand side, one wheel being pressed on each, and put the remaining wheels on as far as they will go without pressing. The pump and lubricator eccentrics are put on their respective axles as they are pushed through the boxes. All the crankpins are set as near as possible to right angles "by eye." The right-hand coupling-rod is then placed over the crankpins on the pressed-home wheels. The left-hand one is applied to the other side, and if the crankpins don't all enter the holes in the bushes, it is a simple matter to adjust the wheels until they do. When both rods are on, and the wheels turn freely without binding anywhere, the rest of the wheels can be pressed right home.

The rods can then be erected, the first and second bosses being prevented from coming off by washers in the recesses, secured by 5 B.A. countersunk screws. To make the washers, chuck a piece of $\frac{1}{2}$ in. round mild steel, face, centre, drill No. 30 to about $\frac{1}{4}$ in. depth, countersunk with No. 2 drill, and part off a 1/16 in. slice. The fourth and fifth bosses only need commercial nuts and washers. The driving bosses require no fixing, as the big-ends of the connecting-rods prevent them straying. Note—all the bushes must be quite free on the pins; no tight places anywhere. The whole ten wheels should spin freely by just turning the driving crankpin by hand, with the wheels off the bench, and the axleboxes in running position with bits of 1/8 in. square rod between axleboxes and hornstays.

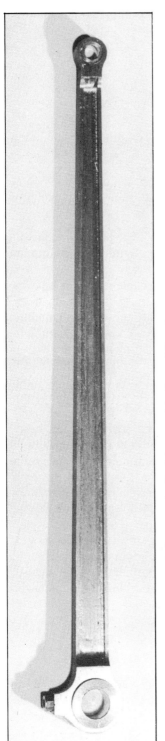

The connecting rod from Mr R H Procter's "Evening Star" (photograph by Lorna Minton)

Left-hand cylinder with crosshead

The top deck and front plate of the tender (photograph by N Sturgess)

CHAPTER FOUR

The Pony Truck

The pony truck on the full-size engine is a complicated box of tricks consisting of bars, plates, brackets, angles and what-have-you, secured by a multitude of bolts and nuts. It would be hopeless to reproduce it as a working proposition in 3.$\frac{1}{2}$ in. gauge; so what I have done is to scheme out a simpler arrangement which bears a family likeness to its big relation, but which is easy to construct, and will stand up to the job. It consists of a steel frame on which the horns are mounted; these are bent from steel strip, and held in place by a cross-bearer at the top. Ordinary axleboxes with overhead springs are fitted to the horns. No side-control springs are needed as the friction between the cross-bearer and the underside of the bolster prevents "hunting" at speed on a straight road, while allowing ample freedom to slide sideways on curves. As big sister's pony simply bristles with nuts and bolts, I've shown the little pony with similar adornments.

A piece of 1/8 in. mild steel plate 6.7/8 in. long and 3.1/8 in. wide is needed for the baseplate or frame. Mark it out to the dimensions shown and saw and file to outline. The triangular hole can be cut by drilling holes all around, breaking out the piece, and cleaning with a file, or it can be cut out with a piercing-saw. That useful tool known as an Abrafile will also make short work of it. As a matter of fact, the hole needn't be cut at all by anybody who doesn't worry about its appearance. To bend the frame, grip it in the vice at the places indicated, and hit the projecting part with a mallet, or what railway shopmen call a "bacon-rind hammer"; that is, one with hide inserts at each end of the head. I always use one, as it leaves no mark on the work. Drill a 9/16 in. hole at the apex, and fit a bronze bush to it as shown. After bushing the coupling-rods, you won't need detailed instructions for that little job!

The Horncheeks

Four 2.$\frac{1}{2}$ in. lengths of 7/16 in. × 3/32 in. mild steel strip will be required for the horncheeks. Bend each at a right angle at 5/8 in. from one end; a job easily done in the bench vice. The second bend is made at 1.3/16 in. from the first and as all four must be exactly alike, bend them over a jig. This is just a piece of steel bar about $\frac{1}{2}$ in. × 1 in., and cut to the length mentioned. Take the sharp edge off

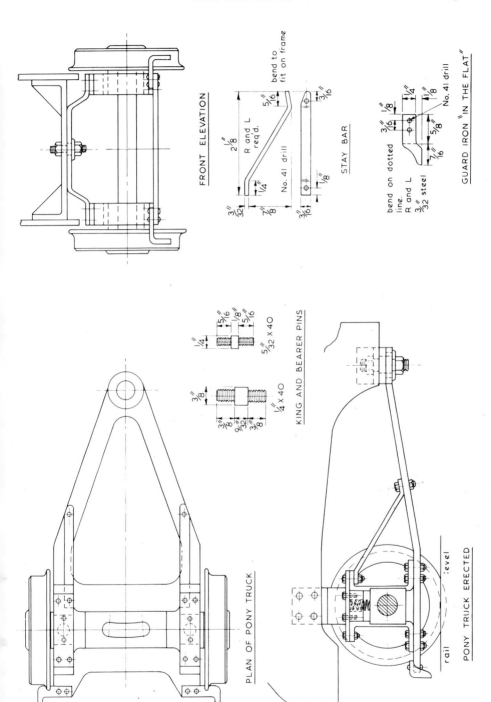

FRONT ELEVATION

STAY BAR

bend to fit on frame

$\frac{5}{16}$"

$2\frac{1}{8}$" R and L req'd.

No. 41 drill

$\frac{3}{32}$" $\frac{7}{8}$" $\frac{3}{16}$"

$\frac{1}{4}$"

$\frac{3}{16}$"

$\frac{1}{8}$"

GUARD IRON "IN THE FLAT"

bend on dotted line.
R and L
$\frac{3}{32}$" steel

$\frac{3}{16}$" $\frac{1}{4}$" $\frac{1}{8}$"

No. 41 drill

$\frac{5}{8}$" $\frac{7}{16}$"

$\frac{1}{8}$"

KING AND BEARER PINS

$\frac{5}{16}$" $\frac{1}{8}$" $\frac{5}{16}$"
$\frac{1}{4}$" $\frac{5}{32}$ x 40

$\frac{3}{8}$" $\frac{1}{4}$ x 40

$\frac{3}{8}$" $\frac{9}{32}$" $\frac{3}{8}$"

PLAN OF PONY TRUCK

PONY TRUCK ERECTED

rail   level

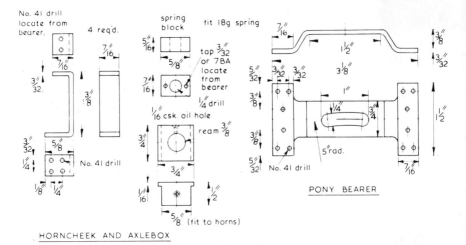

HORNCHEEK AND AXLEBOX

the ends. Rest the jig on the lower bend, and grip in the bench vice. If the upper end is then beaten down on to the jig, the four horns will all be the same height, which is essential. Trim the upper bend to 7/16 in. length, and drill four No. 41 holes in the bottom bend. Leave the holes in the upper bend until the bearer is made and fitted.

The Axleboxes

These can be made either from drawn bronze or gunmetal bar of $\frac{1}{2}$ in. × $\frac{3}{4}$ in. section, or from cast bar. As they are machined up in exactly the same way as the main axleboxes, there is no need to go through the ritual again; but note that they have flanges on one side only. Take care to drill and ream the holes dead square with the faces.

Ordinary brass rod, or mild steel rod of 5/16 in. × 7/16 in. section can be used for the spring blocks. Grip the rod in the four-jaw chuck, and part off two 5/8 in. lengths. Drill a $\frac{1}{4}$ in. hole through the middle of each, as shown.

The Bearer

This can be made from a piece of 1.$\frac{1}{2}$ in. × 3/32 in. mild steel approximately 3.$\frac{3}{4}$ in. long. Mark out as shown, then saw out the two side pieces to leave a $\frac{3}{4}$ in. centre, after which the bearer can be bent to shape in the bench vice, using a bit of 3/8 in. square bar as a gauge to get both bends equal. Trim the ends to bring the overall width to 3.1/8 in. and drill the No. 41 screwholes as shown. Be careful when marking out the curved slot; the radius of the centre-line should be struck out first, through the centre of the bearer, and then the slot can be marked off by lines at each side. To cut the slot, just drill a few 7/32 in. holes along the centre-line, run them into a slot with a round file, and finish to size with a half-round file. A piece of ¼ in. round steel should slide easily from one end to the other. An exact fit doesn't matter, as the pony is controlled by the king pin; the slot merely limits the sideplay.

Wheels and Axle

The pony wheels are 2.¼ in. dia. on treads, with 1/8 in. flanges, and are turned in exactly the same way as described for the coupled wheels; so repetition is not necessary. Same applies to the axles, which are turned from 3/8 in. round mild steel, to the dimensions shown. Oil ducts are not required in the pony axle, as you can poke the spout of an oil feeder between the wheel spokes, and put a drop down the oil holes on top of the axleboxes.

The king pin is also turned from 3/8 in. round steel held in the chuck. Face the end, turn down 3/8 in. length to ¼ in. dia. and screw ¼ in. × 40. Part off at 21/32 in. from the shoulder, reverse in the chuck and repeat the turning and screwing operation on the other end. The bearer pin is turned in the same way, from ¼ in. round rod to the dimensions shown.

As ¼ in. and 5/32 in. × 40 nuts are not made commercially, make those required from hexagon steel or brass rod; 3/8 in. for the king pin and 5/16 in. for the bearer pin. The hexagon rod can be held truly in the three-jaw. Face, centre, drill the larger one 7/32 in. and tap ¼ in. × 40. Drill the smaller one No. 30 and tap 5/32 in. × 40. Chamfer the corners of the hexagon and part off to 3/16 in length.

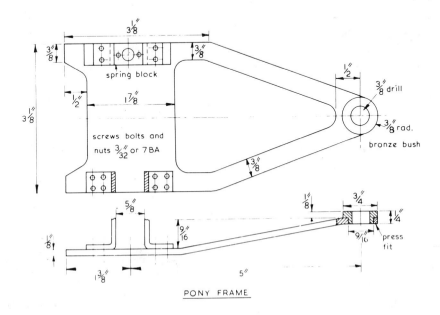

PONY FRAME

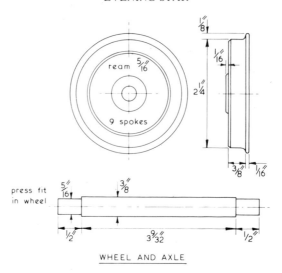

reom 5/16

9 spokes

1/8

1/16

2 1/4

3/8   1/16

press fit
in wheel   5/16   3/8

1/2   3 9/32   1/2

WHEEL AND AXLE

The stay bars are merely pieces of 3/16 in. × 3/32 in. steel strip, bent to the shape shown, and drilled at the ends. The guard irons can also be cut from any odd bit of 3/32 in. steel of requisite size; offcuts kept in a box under the bench, come in mighty handy and save time. Saw and file to outline, bend as indicated, and drill the rivet holes.

Assembly and Erection

The leading horncheeks are set with the rubbing faces at 1/16 in. from the front end of the pony frame, and flush with the sides, as shown in the plan drawing. Set one in position, hold it there with a toolmakers' clamp, and drill the outer bolt holes through the frame with a No. 41 drill, using those in the horn foot as guides. Fix with 7 BA bolts, as shown in the elevation of the assembled pony truck. When locating the second one, be sure to keep it dead in line with the first. Then drill the other bolt holes, and put in the bolts. Another beginners' tip: broken ends of drills can be used to make extension drills for jobs like this. Chuck a piece of 3/16 in. round rod about 3 in. long. Face, centre, and drill for about ¼ in. depth with a drill a size smaller than the broken bit. Hold the latter tightly in the bench vice between two pieces of sheet copper, so that it won't get damaged, and have the broken end projecting. Drive the bit of brass rod on to it, and you have a useful gadget that can be held in the chuck of a hand brace or electric drill, and will reach into all kinds of tight places.

To locate the rear horncheeks, use the axleboxes themselves as spacers. Set the horncheek flush with the edge of the frame, and put the axlebox between it and the one already fixed, so that the box can slide easily between them, but without slackness. Clamp it in place, and then drill the bolt holes and bolt up as before.

Now set the bearer in place on top of the horncheeks, as shown in the front elevation. Clamp it in position with two small clamps, one at each side, holding the top bends of the front horncheeks to the underside of it. Drill the holes in the bends, using those in the bearer as guides, and bolt up. Shift the cramps to the back horncheeks, see that the axleboxes are free to move from top to bottom, and drill as before; but before bolting up, put the staybars in place. The inner bolt at each side goes through the end of the staybar as well as the bearer and horncheek bend, so that longer bolts will be needed. The lower ends of the staybars are bolted to the frame, as shown in the elevation of the pony truck erected.

To fit the spring blocks, put one in place at the top of the horns, put the axleboxes in under it, then jam a wooden wedge or a piece of metal between. This will hold the spring block in place while a No. 41 drill is run through the holes in the bearer, to make countersinks on top of the block. Remove block, drill the countersinks No. 48, tap 7 BA, replaced block and fix with two screws. The springs are wound up from 18-gauge tinned steel wire over a piece of 5/32 in. rod. Wind enough for two, cut off two $\frac{1}{2}$ in. lengths, square off the ends against an emery-wheel, turn the pony upside down on the bench, drop the springs into the holes in the blocks, and insert the axleboxes. The springs should just start to compress when the boxes are in bottom position.

Press one wheel on the axle, push the axle through the boxes, and press on the other wheel. The guard irons are riveted on with 3/32 in rivets as shown, level with the centres of the wheel treads. Put the king and bearer pins in the holes in bolster and stay, and secure with nuts. The pony truck can then be put in place, and the nuts put on, with washers between them and the pony as shown. The pony truck should then be perfectly free to swing from side to side, to the amount allowed by the curved slot.

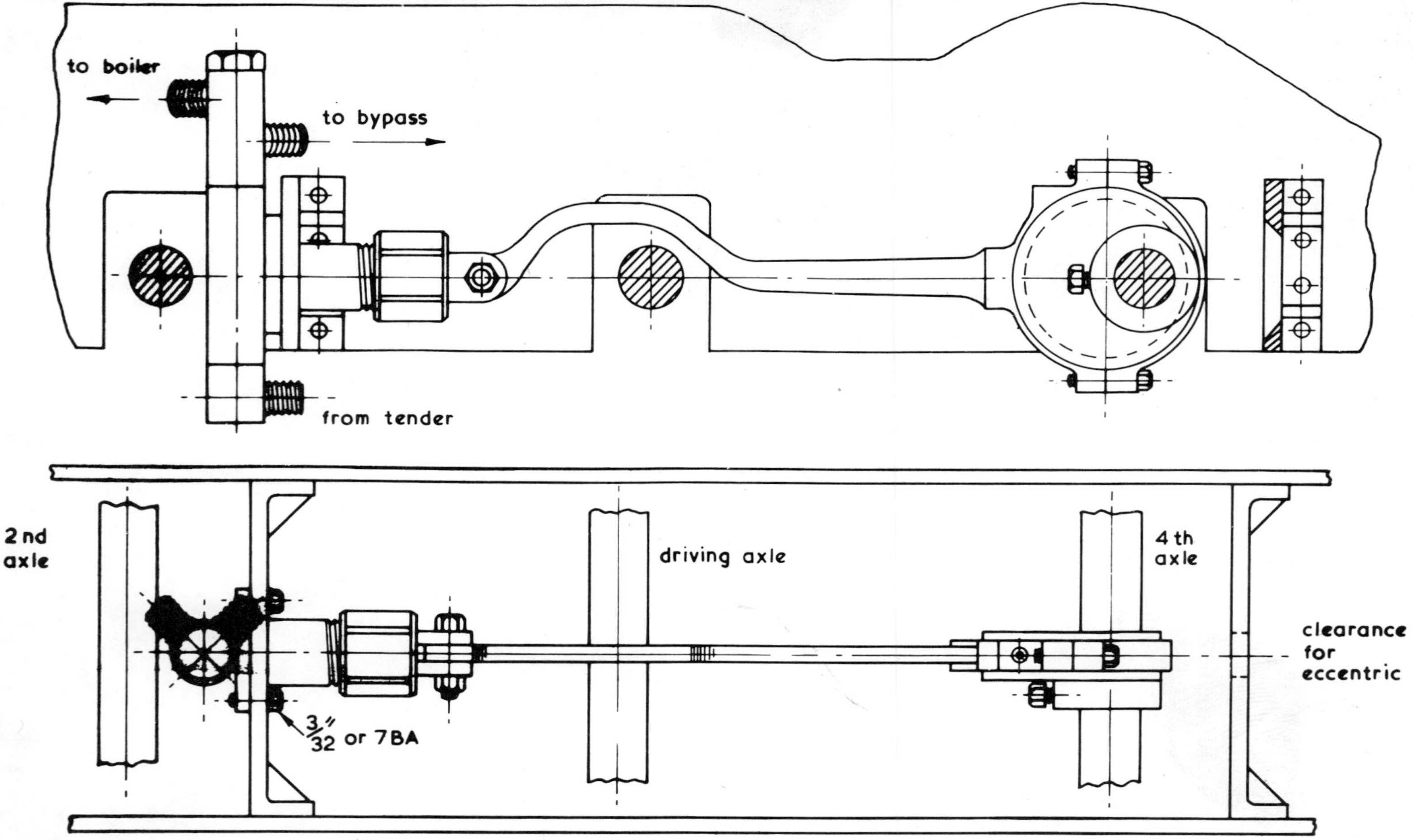

to boiler

to bypass

to bypass

from tender

clearance
for
eccentric

4 th
axle

driving axle

3"/32 or 7BA

2 nd
axle

ELEVATION   PLAN OF PUMP ERECTED

CHAPTER FIVE

The boiler feed pump

The full-size *Evening Star* doesn't possess a boiler feed pump, as her boiler is fed by two injectors, but a pump is very desirable on the little engine. Until Giffard invented the injector, pumps were used on all locomotives, and were driven either from an eccentric, or from the crossheads. They worked all right, but the great disadvantage was that they couldn't feed the boiler while the engine was standing still. When the Stroudley engine No. 189 *Edward Blount* of the L.B. & S.C.R. was shown at the Paris Exhibition of 1889, the judges told Billy Stroudley that she would have taken top award, but for just that one drawback. Billy's reply was "Ah, but my engines are intended for running, not standing still!"

The advantage of a pump on a little locomotive is that while the amount of water it pumps is constant at any given speed, the by-pass valve can be set so that only sufficient water to maintain working level will enter the boiler, the surplus returning to the tank or tender. If an injector is fitted as well, to feed the boiler when stationary (we shall do this on the little *Evening Star*) we have the ideal combination. Continuous feeding by injector only, as in full size, is impossible in 3.½ in. gauge because an injector cannot be made small enough; but an injector such as I shall describe in due course would do the job if used intermittently.

It was my original intention to specify the same type of pump that I designed for *Britannia*. This was very efficient, but as *Evening Star's* wheels, being smaller, turn faster for the same running speed, and there is less room between axles, I schemed out a pump more suitable for the job. It is easily made, and being set on the centre-line of motion, there is ample room for the valve-box and upper pipe connections. By using an eccentric-rod with a set in it, the drive can be taken from the fourth axle, and the length of the rod is sufficient to avoid undue stress and wear on the gland.

Machining the Pump Body

Grip the casting by one end of the valve-box in the four-jaw independent chuck, and set it so that the other end runs truly. Face the end, centre, and drill

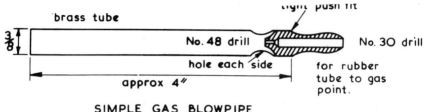

SIMPLE GAS BLOWPIPE

right through with No. 23 drill. Open out for about $\frac{1}{4}$ in. depth with a 9/32 in. drill, and finish to 7/16 in. depth with a 9/32 in. D-bit. This leaves a flat-bottomed hole for the valve ball to sit on. Beginners' tip: make your own D-bit from 2 in. of 9/32 in. round silver-steel. File away half the diameter for $\frac{1}{2}$ in. length, and bevel off the end. Heat to medium red and plunge into clean cold water. Rub the filed part on an oilstone until bright with sharp edges. Hold the unfiled end in a gas or spirit flame, so that the heat will travel down the bit. As soon as the filed end turns dark yellow, drop the bit into the water again, and it is then ready for use. Slightly countersink the end of the valve-box, and tap it 5/16 in. × 32 t.p.i. by the method shown for tapping the short crankpins; but be careful that the tap doesn't go too far in, and cattle up the ball seating! Put a 5/32 in. parallel reamer into the No. 23 drilled hole for about half its length, to true up the D-bitted end, or alternatively, take a scrape out of it with a taper broach.

Chuck a short bit of round rod not less than $\frac{1}{2}$ in. dia. in the three-jaw. Face the end, turn about $\frac{1}{4}$ in. length to 5/16 in. dia. and screw it 5/16 in. × 32 t.p.i. with a die in the tailstock holder. Screw the machined end of the valve-box on to this tightly, and the other end should then run truly. Face the end, open the No. 23 hole to 9/32 in. depth, slightly countersink the end, and tap 5/16 in. × 32 t.p.i. Make a little chisel by filing the end of a couple of inches of 3/32 in. silver-steel, harden and temper it like the D-bit, and make four nicks with it at the end of the hole, like the one shown in the pump section. This is very important, for without the nicks, the ball would lift on the out-stroke of the pump ram, block the hole, and prevent the ram from sucking any water.

The casting will have a chucking-piece on it, opposite the barrel. Grip this in the three-jaw, and set the end of the barrel to run truly. If it wobbles, a slight tap with a hammer will teach it good manners, as the cast metal is fairly ductile. Face the end, so that it stands approximately 1.1/8 in. from the valve-box. Centre, and drill a 3/16 in. pilot hole right through into the valve-box, then open it out with a 3/8 in. drill. Turn the outside to 9/16 in. dia. and screw it for about 3/8 in. length with a 9/16 in. × 32 t.p.i. die in the tailstock holder. Finally, face off the square section next the valve-box with a knife tool, to about 1/8 in. thickness. Saw or part off the chucking-piece, and file the stub flush with the valve-box for neatness sake.

The top fitting carries in addition to the union nipples, a supplementary clack, or check valve, which will prevent steam and water blowing back from the boiler into the tender, in the event of the top feed clack leaking if scale or grit should accidentally get on to the ball seat. To make it, part off a piece of $\frac{1}{2}$ in. rod a full 1.$\frac{1}{4}$ in. long. Use drawn bronze or gunmetal for preference; good quality brass will do at a pinch, but don't use the alloy known in the metal trade as "screw-rod", which is very often sold as brass. This is intended for making screws, as its name implies, and takes an excellent clean thread, but is inferior to bronze or gunmetal. It is, however, quite suitable for screwed pipe nipples, and other fitments where there is no movement.

Chuck the rod in the three-jaw, face, centre, and drill through with No. 23 drill, then proceed exactly as described for the upper end of the valve-box. Reverse in chuck, turn $\frac{1}{4}$ in. of the other end to 5/16 in. dia. and screw 5/16 in × 32 t.p.i. Drop a 7/32 in. rustless steel ball into the valve-box, and take the depth from ball to top of box with a depth gauge.

Face off the screwed spigot until it is 1/32 in. less than the distance indicated by the depth gauge, then cross-nick the end with a thin flat file, as shown. To get the correct location of the union nipples, screw the fitting tightly into the top of the valve-box, after which, the position of each one can be marked off as shown in the drawings, 45 deg. off centre-line, and at right angles to each other. Centre-pop each location, remove the fitting, and drill an 11/64 in. hold at each pop. For the nipples, chuck a piece of 5/16 in. round rod, face the end, centre deeply with a size D centre-drill, then drill to 3/8 in. depth with No. 30 drill.

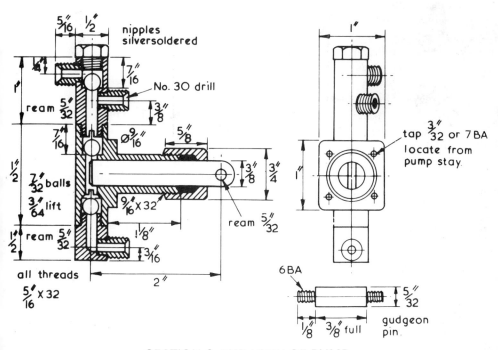

SECTION & END VIEW OF PUMP

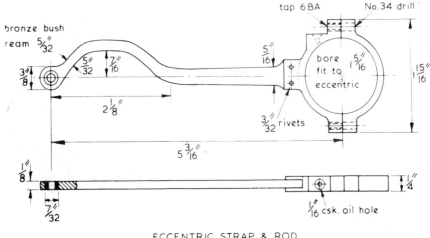

ECCENTRIC STRAP & ROD

Screw ¼ in. of the outside 5/16 in. × 32 t.p.i. part off at 5/16 in. from the end, reverse in the chuck, it won't hurt the threads as long as you don't wrench the chuck key—and turn the plain end to a tight fit in the hole in the side of the fitting. About 1/16 in. length will be plenty. Press the spigots into the holes, and silversolder them.

I silversolder all my small fittings with a home-made gas torch, which any beginner can make in 15 minutes or less. It is just a 4 in. length of 3/8 in. tube with a brass nipple pushed into one end, two air holes being filed in it and it is connected to the domestic gas supply by a rubber tube. It is self-blowing and will provide enough heat to do all the small jobs on *Evening Star*. I use Johnson-Matthey's "Easyflo" wire, and the flux sold for use with it. Mix a little with water, to a creamy paste, and smear some all around the joint between nipples and fitting. A tin lid with a layer of coke broken into little bits makes a nobby brazing tray. Lay the fitting in it, heat to medium red, and touch the joint with a piece of "Easyflo" wire. This will immediately melt, and run around the joint like water. Let cool to black, and quench out in acid pickle. For this I use a jam-jar half filled with a mixture of one part stale accumulator acid to four of tap water. After pickling for about ten minutes, fish out the fitting with a piece of wire, wash well in running water, and clean up. I hold them against a 4 in. circular wire brush, the spindle of which is fitted into a hole in the end of the spindle of my tool grinder. It makes them bobby-dazzle!

Bottom Fitting

Chuck a ¾ in. length of ½ in. round rod; face, centre, drill to 5/8 in. depth with No. 23 drill, and ream or broach as previously mentioned. Drop a 7/32 in. ball into the recess in the valve-box, take the depth as before, and turn down the end of the rod to 5/16 in. dia. and to a length 1/32 in. less than the depth indicated by the gauge. Screw 5/16 in. × 32 t.p.i. Screw this tightly into the bottom of the valve-box, and mark the position of the nipple, parallel with the pump barrel. Centre-pop, drill 11/64 in. and fit a nipple as described above.

To assemble, first seat the balls by putting them on the holes, resting a short piece of brass rod on each, and giving it one good crack with a hammer. That prevents water leaking back when the pump is working. Screw the fittings home with a slight smear of plumbers' jointing (Boss White or similar) on the threads, but don't let any get on the ball seatings. The plug for the top of the upper fitting is made from 3/8 in. hexagon rod. Chuck in three-jaw, face off, turn the spigot to 5/16 in. dia. and $\frac{1}{4}$ in. length, screw 5/16 in. × 32 t.p.i., face off the end sufficiently to allow the ball 3/64 in. lift, part off at 3/16 in. from the shoulder, reverse in chuck and chamfer the corners of the hexagon.

Ram and Gland

The ram is a $2.\frac{1}{4}$ in. length of 3/8 in. ground rustless steel or drawn bronze, and should be a sliding fit in the barrel, needing no turning. Slightly chamfer one end, and at 2 in. from it drill a No. 23 cross-hole. Make certain this goes right across the centre-line, and not to one side; it is merely a matter of care. Cut a slot 1/8 in. wide and 7/16 in. deep, at right angles to the cross-hole, by the method described for slotting the forks of the coupling-rods; then ream the cross-hole 5/32 in.

For the gland, chuck a piece of $\frac{3}{4}$ in. round or hexagon rod, face, centre, and drill 3/8 in. to $\frac{3}{4}$ in. depth. Open out to $\frac{1}{2}$ in. depth with $\frac{1}{2}$ in. drill, and tap 9/16 in. × 32 t.p.i. Chamfer the edge, part off at 5/8 in. from the end, reverse in chuck, and chamfer. If round rod is used, four slots can be milled in the outside as shown, which will enable a C-spanner to be used for tightening.

Erection

Take out the pump stay, push the pump barrel through the hole in it, set the valve-box vertical, temporarily clamp in position with the square pad tight against the stay, and run a No. 41 drill through the screwholes in the stay, making countersinks in the pad. Remove the pump, drill the countersinks No. 48, tap 7 BA, replace pump and secure with hexagon-head screws as shown in plan. Note that the pump is fixed to the stay with the valve-box on the opposite side to the stay flanges. The pump gland can then be packed. The best kind of packing would be a few strands unravelled from a piece of full-size hydraulic pump packing; failing that, use graphited yarn. The gland should only be tightened sufficiently to prevent water leaking past. A too-tight gland only causes unnecessary friction. The stay with pump attached can then be put back in the frame.

Eccentric Strap and Rod

Any roughness on the casting for the eccentric strap should be removed with a file, and the two lugs drilled No. 44. Scribe a line across the centre of the lugs, and grip the casting in the bench vice with the line just showing. Saw across the lugs, keeping the saw blade pressed down on the vice top, to ensure a straight cut. Smooth off any saw-marks, then open out the holes in the "ring" half with No. 34 drill, and tap those in the "lug" half 6BA. Join the two halves with 6 BA screws, and chuck the strap in the four-jaw with the cored hole running as truly as possible, letting about 1/16 in. overhang. Face off the side of the strap with a round-nose tool set crosswise in the tool-holder, then change it for a boring-tool, and bore the strap to an easy fit on the eccentric. I always use a piece of round steel turned to the same diameter as the eccentric for a gauge, which also can be used as a mandrel for facing the other side of the strap. Just clamp it on by its own screws, putting a strip of paper between the strap and mandrel, to prevent slipping; then grip the mandrel in the three-jaw, and go ahead with the facing, until the strap is just wide enough to fit nicely between the eccentric flanges. Drill a 1/16 in. oil hole in the step on the casting, and countersink it. The side lug can be slotted for the rod, by clamping it in a machine-vice at the requisite height on the lathe saddle, and running it under the cutter used for slotting the coupling-rod forks.

The easiest way to make the rod, and ensure accuracy of the set in it, is to mark it out on a piece of 1/8 in. frame steel, and saw and file to the marked outline. This saves any bending, which is always a time-wasting process of trial and error. The round end is drilled 7/32 in. and bronze-bushed like the coupling-rods. The other end is fitted into the slot in the strap, and secured by a couple of 3/32 in. rivets, countersunk both sides. It may be soldered in addition, which will prevent the rivets working loose. The little end is attached to the pump ram by a gudgeon-pin, which is merely a piece of 5/32 in. silver-steel turned down at each end to 7/64 in. dia. and screwed 6 BA as shown, commercial nuts being used. When they are tight against the shoulders, it should still be possible to twist the pin with your fingers when it is in position in the ram.

A slot will be needed in the back frame stay, to allow for eccentric clearance. Mark out and drill three 11/32 in. holes on the centre-line, run them into a slot with a round file, and finish to shape shown with a square one.

Side view of chassis   (photograph by K Pietron)

Aerial view of chassis   (photograph by K Pietron)

Underside of boiler showing combustion chamber and water tubes
(photograph by N Sturgess)

The boiler – nearly complete
(photograph by N Sturgess)

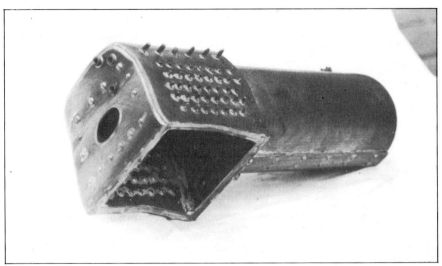

CHAPTER SIX

The piston valve cylinders

Builders of *Evening Star* have the choice of fitting either piston-valve or slide-valve cylinders. The full-size engine has, of course, piston-valve cylinders with long-travel valves, and this is the kind I prefer. At the same time, some folk—especially beginners—seem scared of tackling piston-valves because it is essential that the bobbins on the valves should be turned to an exact fit in the steam-chest liners. Actually, the job is no more difficult than turning the pistons to fit the cyclinder bores, and that has to be done anyway, so why worry? However, I will describe a suitable pair of slide-valve cylinders for the benefit of those who prefer that type. No alterations will be required in the dimensions of the valve gear. Simply reverse the connections at the top of the combination lever, and set the return cranks to lead the main cranks instead of following them.

On lathes of the Myford type, the easiest way of setting up the cylinder casting for boring and facing is to mount it on an angle-plate. If the contact side of the casting isn't flat, smooth it off with a file. Check the location of the two core-holes. If they are much out, smooth off one end of the casting with a file, plug the ends of the coreholes with bits of wood, mark out the correct centres of the bores on the wood, coat the cleaned-up end of the casting with marking-out fluid, and strike two circles showing the main and steam-chest bores, with a pair of dividers. Bolt an angle-plate to the lathe faceplate, and put the cylinder casting on it, securing it with a bar across its back, held down with a bolt at each end. If the slots in the angleplate don't come right for the bolts, drill holes in the angleplate to suit.

Set the casting at right angles to the faceplate—easily done by application of a try-square—letting the end overhang the angleplate by $\frac{1}{4}$ in. or so; then tighten the clamp bolts. Next set the larger corehole, or the marked circle, as the case may be, so that it runs truly. If the bolts holding the angleplate to the faceplate are left just slack enough to allow the angleplate to be moved, this is an easy job. I can set it by eye, in two wags of a dog's tail, having done so many of them; but a scribing-block, or surface-gauge, standing on the saddle or lathe bed, with the needle set to the edge of the corehole or marked circle, will show at a glance the amount and direction of adjustment needed. Be careful to avoid moving it when tightening the bolts.

The assembly is well off the faceplate centre, and if the lathe is started, there will be a fine imitation of an earthquake in the workshop. To prevent this, bolt a balance-weight of some sort to the faceplate, opposite the assembly. I use lead weights of various sizes and diameters, cast in lids of discarded tin cans, or in cut-down cans; the melted lead is poured in, left to cool, and then drilled $\frac{1}{4}$ in. or so through the middle. Slip the lathe belt off the pulley, and spin the mandrel by hand; you'll soon see if the job is balanced sufficiently.

With a roundnose tool set crosswise in the sliderest tool-holder, face off the end of the casting, taking off half the difference between length of casting and finished job. Then set up a good stiff boring tool, and take a cut through the bore sufficiently deep to get well under the skin of the casting. Run at fairly slow speed, to avoid tool chatter, and have the cutting edge of the tool slightly above the centre-line, to avoid rubbing. Myford and similar lathes have self-acting movement to the saddle, and this should be used, with the gearwheels set up to give the finest available feed. If there is no self-act, the top slide must be used, and set so that it produces a parallel bore, before the casting is set up. This is easy. Chuck a piece of rod about $\frac{3}{4}$ in. dia. in the three-jaw, with about 2.$\frac{1}{2}$ in. projecting. Set the top slide parallel with it, as near as you can judge, and with a narrow-ended roundnose tool, take a fine cut 1/64 in. or less, along the rod. Take the diameter of this at each end with a micrometer or a pair of calipers. If the "mike" shows a variation of half a division (0.0005 in.) or less, or you can't detect any difference in the feel of the calipers, the slide is O.K. for the boring job. If there is any variation, adjust the top slide and repeat operation until you get it right. It will be time well spent as the bores must be parallel.

If a 1.$\frac{1}{4}$ in. parallel reamer is available, bore until the business end of the reamer will just enter. If not, bore to finished diameter, taking the last two cuts without shifting the cross-slide. Then slacken the bolts holding the angleplate

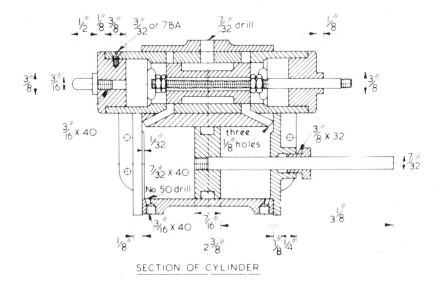

SECTION OF CYLINDER

to the faceplate, and move the whole assembly until the steam-chest corehole, or marked circle is running truly; tighten the bolts and repeat the boring operation. Don't on any account slacken the bolts holding the clamp bar, or the two bores will be out of line. To face off the other end of the casting, chuck a piece of rod a little over $1.\frac{1}{4}$ in. dia. and turn about 1 in. of it to a tight fit in the cylinder bore. Put the cylinder on it, rough end outwards, and face off with a roundnose tool until the casting is 2.3/8 in. overall length. It is advisable to centre the rod with a centre-drill in the tailstock chuck, and support it with the tailstock centre while facing off, owing to the overhang. I use a Lecount expanding mandrel for this job, but such gadgets are not usually found in home workshops—too expensive nowadays!

Contact Side and Passages

Up-end the cylinder on the angleplate, putting a piece of thin sheet copper under it to prevent damaging the end. Fix it with a long bolt through the main bore, with a big washer and another bit of thin copper under the nut. Set the contact side parallel to the faceplate; a depth gauge applied at each end easily does that. Adjust the angleplate until the casting is central with the faceplate, to maintain as good balance as possible, then face off with a roundnose tool until the contact side is exactly $\frac{1}{4}$ in. from the edge of the main bore, as shown in the cross section.

If the passages between cylinder bore and steam-chest are not cored out in the casting, they must be drilled. File a flat in the edge of the bore, opposite the steam-chest, a full 3/8 in. long and 1/8 in. wide. Hold the casting in a machine-vice on the drilling-machine table, set at such an angle that the line of the passage-ways will be vertical. Then drill with 1/8 in. or No. 32 drill, into the bore of the steam-chest. The holes can also be drilled by hand, if the casting is held in the bench vice so that the line of the holes is horizontal. If the hand brace is then held horizontally, the holes will break through into the steam-chest in the right place.

Steam-chest Liners

The liners can be turned either from castings, or from drawn bronze or gunmetal rod 1.1/8 in. dia. Cored stick, as used for making bearing bushes in automobile and similar work, can also be used, as it resists both heat and water. Two pieces $3.\frac{3}{4}$ in. long are needed. Chuck in the three-jaw and if solid rod or casting is used, face the end, centre, put a pilot hole through with $\frac{1}{4}$ in. drill, then open out with 5/8 in. drill. A cored casting, or piece of cored stick, should be opened up with a boring tool, in the same way as the cylinder casting was bored.

Next mount the liner on a mandrel between centres. A piece of $\frac{3}{4}$ in. round rod about 5 in. long is centre-drilled at each end, put between lathe centres with

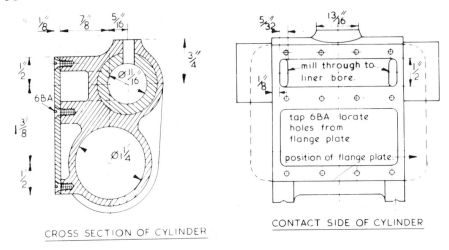

CROSS SECTION OF CYLINDER   CONTACT SIDE OF CYLINDER

a carrier on one end, and about 4 in. of it turned down to a tight fit in the liner blank. Drive the liner on to it, not too tightly or you may damage it when getting it off. Put the lot between centres, and turn the outside of the liner to a press fit in the steam-chest bore, by the method I have already described for turning pins and wheel seats to a press fit, viz. turn about 1/8 in. of the end to a tight push handle within half-a-division of its original setting. If the lathe has no self-act, the top slide must be set to turn parallel by aid of "mike" or calipers applied to the ends of the liner.

Remove from mandrel, and chuck in three-jaw as truly as possible. Take a facing skim off the end, then bore to 13/16 in. dia. for $\frac{3}{4}$ in. depth. Turn in end-for-end, and repeat the operation, bringing the overall length to 3.5/8 in. Now be very careful about the next bit. At 1.1/16 in. from the end, turn a groove 5/32 in. wide and 1/16 in. deep, with a parting-tool, and at 1.3/16 in. farther along, turn another similar groove. The important thing is, that the width of the grooves, and the distance between the inner edges, must be exactly as shown, as they locate the steam ports. If a milling-machine is available, put a saw-type cutter 5/32 in. wide on the arbor, grip the liner in a machine-vice on the table, and mill straight across the grooves again, so that the slots are exactly opposite, as shown in the cross-section of the liner. The openings left by the cutter in the bore of the liner, form the ports.

The job can be done in the lathe in similar fashion, with a 5/32 in. cutter on a spindle between centres, and the liner held in a machine-vice at correct height, with the vice bolted to the lathe saddle. The slots may also be hand-filed with a thin flat file, the liner being held in the bench vice, bits of soft copper sheet being put between jaws and liner, to prevent damage. Chuck the liner again, and bore out the centre part to a shade under 11/16 in. dia. so that the slightly-tapered end of an 11/16 in. parallel reamer will just enter. Finally, file two clearances across the outer ends of the grooves, as shown in the drawing, to allow steam from the ports to get to the passages in the cylinder.

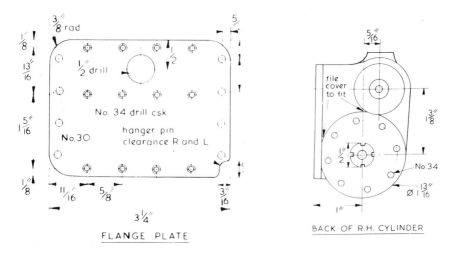

FLANGE PLATE

BACK OF R.H. CYLINDER

The liners can then be pressed into the steam-chest bores in the cylinder castings, using the vice as press, as previously described. Put pieces of soft sheet copper between jaws, and ends of liner and cylinders. Take great care to insert the slightly-reduced end of the liner in such a position that the clearances will line up with the passages in the cylinder when the liner is right home. Press in the liner until the entering end has gone right to the end of the cylinder. As the end projects through the casting for 5/8 in. length, a block of metal or a piece of thick-walled tube at least ¾ in. long, with a 1.1/8 in. hole in it, must now be placed between the end of the cylinder and the vice jaw, where the end of the liner will come through. The pressing can then be completed, the end of the liner entering the hole in the distance-piece as it emerges from the cylinder. Both ends should stand out exactly 5/8 in. from the cylinder.

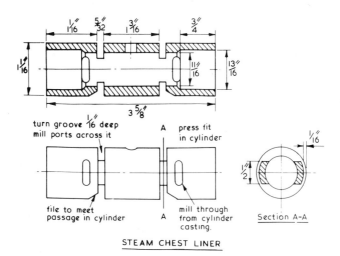

turn groove 1/16 deep
mill ports across it

press fit
in cylinder

file to meet
passage in cylinder

mill through
from cylinder
casting.

Section A-A

STEAM CHEST LINER

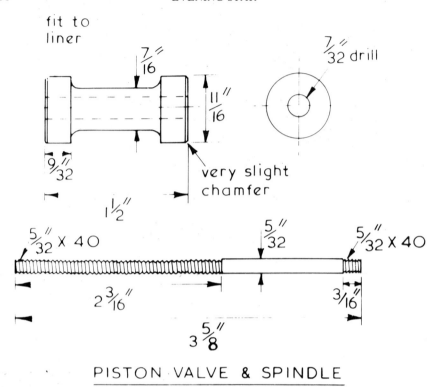

PISTON VALVE & SPINDLE

Reaming by Hand

The reaming should, by the good rights, be done in the lathe, when the cylinder is set up for boring; but the hole through the mandrel of Myford or similar lathes usually found in home workshops, is far too small to allow reamers of the requisite sizes to be put through the bores. The only thing to do is to ream by hand. Grip the cylinder in the bench vice, setting it level. Put a big tapwrench on the end of the reamer shank, enter it in the bore, and slowly turn and push at the same time. The great thing to watch is avoiding any side or down pressure on the reamer, otherwise the bore will either become bell-mouthed or tapered. Hold the tapwrench loosely as it is turned and pushed, so that it kind of "goes its own way." A drop of cutting oil is a great help in getting a smooth finish. Don't attempt to reverse the reamer and pull it out, carry on until the business end goes right through the bore; then take off the wrench, and remove the reamer from the far end of the bore.

The narrow part of the liners can be reamed in the same way. It may be thought by inexperienced workers that these might have been reamed before pressing in, but pressing always causes slight distortion, so it is preferable to ream after pressing.

There will be an oval boss on top of the casting, to which the steam pipe is attached. Smooth this off with a file, centrepop it, and drill an 11/32 in. hole right through into the liner. The exhaust ways are cut through into the liner from the extreme ends of the upper recess in the contact side of the cylinder. These may be slot-drilled. Bolt an angleplate to the vertical slide on the lathe saddle, and set the cylinder end-up on it, securing with a bolt through the bore as previously described. The contact face is set at right angles to lathe centres; put on the faceplate temporarily, and when the contact face is parallel to it, setting it O.K. A 5/32 in. slot drill with just two cutting edges, held in the chuck, is the best tool for a quick clean cut. Adjust the vertical slide until the slot-drill is at the extreme end of the recess, then feed into cut by moving the lathe saddle, and traverse the casting across the slot-drill by moving the cross-slide. Cut the slot at the other end of the recess in the same way, and put the reamer through the liner again to remove any burring.

If a vertical slide isn't available, the job can be done by hand. Drill three 5/32 in. holes at the extreme ends of the recess, right through into the liner, and run them into a slot with a rat-tail file. Their exact position doesn't matter, as all they do is to let the steam out. The admission and exhaust are controlled by the piston-valve sliding over the ports.

Alternative Slide-Valve Cylinders

If I now give a few hints on machining the castings for the alternative slide-valve cylinders, we can take the valves, pistons, covers and glands for both types together. The method of mounting and boring the castings is pretty much the same. Bolt an angleplate to the lathe faceplate, and set the casting on it, contact face down, securing with a bar across its back as previously described. Adjust so that the corehole runs truly, and is parallel to the centre-line of the lathe. Tighten the bolts, then go right ahead as before, facing off the end, and boring to diameter shown. Mount on a mandrel as previously described, for facing the other end.

There are two flat faces to machine off on the slide-valve cylinder castings, against the one face on the piston-valve type, and these must be exactly at right angles. First of all, up-end the cylinder on the angle-plate as described for the piston-valve type, and tool off the contact face until it is $\frac{1}{4}$ in. from the edge of the bore. Then slew the casting around for a quarter-turn, so that the portface is now at right angles to the lathe centre-line. To get it exact, apply a try-square as shown, stock to faceplate, and blade to the machined contact face. Tighten the clamp nut, and tool off the portface until it is 3/8 in. from the edge of the bore.

Coat the portface with marking-out fluid, scribe a line on it at 11/16 in. from the edge opposite to the contact face, and on this line set out the ports. I have arranged the dimensions of them to suit the valve gear specified for the piston-valve cylinders, so that the locomotive will be just as powerful and speedy. To cut the ports, bolt an angleplate to the vertical slide, and fix the cylinder on it, end-up with a bolt through the bore, setting the portface at right angles to the lathe centre-line. This is done in a jiffy by putting on the lathe faceplate, and running the casting up to it until the portface touches the faceplate all over; then tighten the clamp bolt. Put on the three-jaw chuck with a 5/32 in. slot-drill or endmill in it. Adjust the vertical slide until one of the steam port markings is exactly in line with the cutter—and by "exactly," I mean just that. If the ports are "apple-pied," the engine won't give its full efficiency.

Now watch your step. Feed the casting on to the cutter (which should run at a fairly high speed) by moving the saddle towards the lathe headstock until the cutter penetrates about 1/16 in. Now traverse the casting across the cutter by moving the cross-slide handle, and make quite certain that you don't "over-shoot the platform," as the enginemen say; that is, traverse too far so that the cutter goes beyond the ends of the port markings. The easiest way for beginners and inexperienced workers to avoid disaster, is to set the slide with the cutter at each end of the port mark before feeding into cut, and carefully noting the position of the cross-slide handle. If the handle is then brought to the same place every time when cutting, everything in the garden will be lovely.

As the ports are $\frac{1}{4}$ in. depth, feed into cut for another 1/16 in. depth after making the first traverse. Two more doses of the same medicine will bring the port to full required depth. It is better to cut each port by stages, than attempt to cut full depth at one go, because the chances are 1,000 to one, that the side pressure will cause the cutter to spring. The resulting port will be about as straight as a banana.

Adjust the vertical slide until the second steam port is in the right position for cutting, then ditto repeato operations, taking the same strict caution as before. Finally, tackle the exhaust port. This merchant is double the width of the steam ports, but the same cutter will do the trick; just take two cuts, first setting the cutter to one edge, and then to the other. The little bit in between the cuts can be removed by setting the cutter right at each extreme and to full depth, and moving the vertical slide up and down, again taking the utmost care to avoid overrunning the ends.

Steam and Exhaust Passages

The steam passages between the ports and the edges of the cylinder bores are drilled exactly as described for the piston-valve cylinders, with the casting held in a machine-vice on the table of the drilling machine, and set at such an angle that the drill (No. 34 in this case) will break into the port close to the bottom. Set the machine-vice with the casting in it, just clear of the drill; pull down the handle so that the drill comes down outside the casting, and you'll see at a glance if the angle is correct.

Mark off the location of the exhaust way on the contact face, 5/16 in. from the top of the vertical centre-line. Make a deep centrepop, grip the casting in the machine-vice with the contact face level with the jaw tops, and drill a 5/16

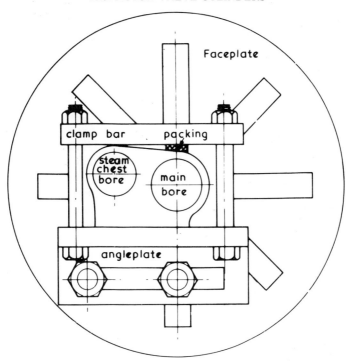

CYLINDER CASTING SET UP FOR BORING
(shift complete assembly to bore steam chest)

in. hole 3/8 in. deep. From the bottom corner of the exhaust port, drill a $\frac{1}{4}$ in. hole breaking into the 5/16 in. hole, as shown in the cross-section. This can also be done with the casting held at the correct angle in the machine-vice. The portface can then be trued up by rubbing it on a piece of fine emerycloth or similar abrasive laid business side up on a surfaceplate, piece of plate glass, or something equally flat and true. The resulting matt finish is the finest working surface you could have, as the microscopic scratches hold a film of oil, over which the valve slides like a skater on a frozen pond.

Steam Chest

The steam chest may be a plain rectangular casting with the bosses screwed in, or the bosses may be cast integral. The outside of the first-mentioned should be cleaned up with a file, gripped in the four-jaw independent chuck, and each side faced off sufficient to bring the finished depth to 11/16 in. On each shorter side, at 9/16 in. from one edge and 1/32 in. from the middle of the width, drill a No. 30 pilot hole, open it out with letter R or 11/32 in. drill, and tap 3/8 in. × 32.

The drill and tap must go through dead square with the sides. I usually hold the steam chest in the machine-vice on the drill table, put the tap in the chuck and start it by turning the drill spindle by hand, which starts it truly. The screwholes in the walls can then be set out, centrepopped and drilled No. 34. Smooth off any burring by rubbing on a piece of emerycloth as mentioned for truing up the port faces.

The bosses are turned from 1 in. round bronze or gunmetal rod. Chuck a piece in three-jaw, face, centre, drill to a full 7/8 in. depth with No. 21 drill, turn ¼ in. of the outside to 3/8 in. dia. and screw 3/8 in. × 32. Part off at a full 5/8 in. from the shoulder, reverse in chuck and take a slight skim off the end, to true it up. One boss is then tapped 3/16 in. × 40 for 3/8 in. depth. The other is opened out with letter R or 11/32 in. drill for ½ in. depth, and tapped 3/8 in. × 32. Screw the bosses tightly into the steam chest, with a smear of plumbers' jointing on the threads. Should the threads be slack (taps and dies don't always cut exactly to size, especially when worn) don't use the jointing, but sweat them in with soft solder after screwing. This is quite O.K. as they never have to be removed.

To machine a chest with integral bosses, chuck by one boss in the three-jaw, and set the other to run truly. Centre it with a centre-drill in the tailstock chuck, then put the centre-point in the tailstock and use it to support the boss while turning it to size and facing off to length, as far as the point will allow. Then put the tailstock chuck back, drill the boss right through with No. 21 drill, tap 3/16 in. × 40 for 3/8 in. depth, and take a slight truing-up skim off the end. Reverse in chuck, and grip by the machined boss; repeat operations on the other one, but this time, after drilling, open out and tap for the gland, as described for the separate boss.

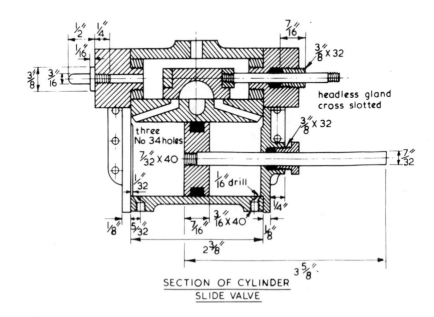

SECTION OF CYLINDER
SLIDE VALVE

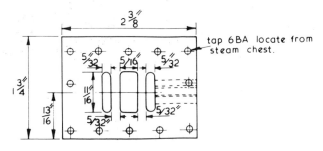

CYLINDER PORT FACE

If the milling machine is available, milling off the top and bottom is a piece of cake, holding the casting in a machine-vice on the table, and running it under a slabbing cutter on the arbor. If not, use the lathe with the machine-vice bolted to the saddle, and the casting set at such a height that a cutter on an arbor between centres, will true up the face of the casting between the bosses. Use the widest cutter available, and take sufficient cuts to cover the whole surface.

Careful hand work would also do it, holding the casting in the bench-vice, and smoothing the face between the bosses with a big flat second-cut file held horizontally. Incidentally, anyone not possessing a vertical slide, could cut the ports by hand. Just drill 1/8 in. holes ¼ in. deep inside the marked lines of the ports; one row for the steam ports, and two for the exhaust. Chip away the surplus metal between the holes, with a couple of little chisels made from silver-steel ¼ in. wide for the sides, and 1/8 in. wide for the ends, which may be left square instead of rounded. Take care to avoid chipping outside the marked lines, and making the ports too wide.

For the gland, chuck a piece of ½ in. round bronze or gunmetal rod, face, centre, and drill to ½ in. depth with No. 21 drill. Turn ½ in. of the outside to 3/8 in. dia. and screw 3/8 in. × 32. Note—the thread must be a very good fit in the steam chest boss, so that the gland doesn't work out when the engine is running. Part off at 7/16 in. from the end, and cross-slot one end with a thin flat file such as used for key cutting.

The steam chest cover will have a boss cast on it for attachment of the steampipe flange, corresponding to the boss on top of the piston-valve cylinder. Face this off and drill it 7/32 in. Leave the screwholes for the time being; they are located when erecting the steam pipes. Chuck the cover in the four-jaw, and face off the plain side. Put it on the steam chest, clamp chest and cover together, and drill the holes in the cover, using those in the steam chest as guides. Countersink them on the flange side of the cover, then round off the outer edge for appearance sake, as shown in the end view of finished cylinder.

Clamp the steam chest to the portface of the cylinder with the outer edges flush, as shown in the end view and cross-section. Run a No. 34 drill through the holes in the steam chest, making countersinks on the portface. Remove chest, grip the cylinder in a machine-vice on the drilling-machine table, with the portface horizontal. Drill the countersinks No. 44, to 3/16 in. depth. The middle hole on the inner side will pierce the exhaust way, which doesn't matter an Aswan; and the drill can be run right through the lip on the outer side, which makes tapping easier. Tap the lot 6 BA, and be mighty careful to avoid breaking the tap in the blind holes. It is easily done; stop immediately you feel any resistance.

Cylinder Covers

The only difference between the covers for the p-v and s-v cylinders is that the latter are 1/16 in. less in diameter. Chuck by the spigot, and set to run as truly as possible; any wobbling is easily cured by a tap with a hammer, as the metal is ductile. Turn the edge to diameter shown, face off, and with a knife tool, carefully cut back the rim for 1/32 in. leaving a projection or register that will fit the cylinder bore without shake. This is very important on the back covers. Leave the front covers solid, but centre the back covers, and run a 7/32 in. drill through them.

The best way to hold the covers for turning the outsides, is to put them in a stepped bush in the three-jaw. A metal ring (any kind except aluminium would do) approximately $2.\frac{1}{4}$ in. dia. and 3/8 in. thick, will be needed for the bush. Maybe our advertisers can supply a casting, with a 1.3/8 in. hole through it. Chuck this as truly as possible in the three-jaw, face it off and turn a step in it about $\frac{1}{4}$ in. deep and 3/16 in. long. Reverse in chuck and grip by the step. Face off, then with a knife tool set crosswise in the toolholder, working from the hole outwards, turn a recess 3/32 in. deep, to the exact diameter of the cover, which should fit the recess without a vestige of shake. Put a centrepop on the face of the ring or bush opposite No. 1 chuck jaw. Remove from chuck, slit one side of the ring with a hacksaw, and replace with the pop mark opposite No. 1 jaw. Should there be any burr at the sawcut, scrape it off, then put the cover in the recess, making sure that the turned side of the cover is pressed tightly home against the back. If the chuck jaws are now tightened, the cover will be held both tight and true.

The front covers only need facing off to 1/8 in. thickness, and very slightly chamfering, just enough to take off the sharp edge. The back covers are also faced to the same thickness, but the boss is turned to $\frac{1}{2}$ in. dia. and faced off so that it stands $\frac{1}{4}$ in. proud of the cover; see longitudinal section. The centre hole should be opened out for tapping with a pin-drill as it is essential for easy working that the gland should be true with the hole. An ordinary drill doesn't always follow a smaller hole truly, and if the holes in gland and cover don't line up, the piston-rod will bind. The pin-drill should be 21/64 in. dia. with a 7/32 in. pilot, and is easily home-made from a bit of 3/8 in. silver-steel, about 3 in. long. Chuck in three-jaw and turn about $\frac{3}{4}$ in. length to diameter given. Face, centre, and drill to 3/8 in. depth with No. 31 drill. File away each side to meet the hole, back off the end at each side to form cutting edges, harden and temper to dark yellow (same process as described for D-bits), press $\frac{3}{4}$ in. of 1/8 in. silver-steel into the hole, and put a 7/32 in. bush over the end to fit the hole in the cover boss, and you're all set.

Put the pin-drill in the tailstock chuck and drill the boss on the cover to 5/16 in. depth, then tap 3/8 in. × 32, guiding the tap with the tailstock as described for tapping crankpins. Turn the glands from $\frac{1}{2}$ in. bronze or gunmetal rod, round or hexagon as desired. Chuck a piece, face, centre, drill No. 21 for 5/8 in. depth, turn 5/16 in. length to 3/8 in. dia. and screw 3/8 in. × 32. Part off at 1/8 in. from shoulder. If round rod is used, file or mill four C-spanner slots in the head.

Drill the screw holes by jig. Get a steel washer the size of the cover, chuck it, and bore the hole to a tight fit on the register that fits in the cylinder bore. Set out and drill No. 34 holes in the washer, as shown on the cover in the back view of cylinder. Put the drilled washer over the register, hold it tightly to the cover with a toolmaker's clamp, and drill the holes in the cover, using those in the washer as guides. This saves bags of time!

The covers for the p-v cylinders will need filing at the points indicated in the drawing, to clear the flange plates and steam-chest bosses. Those for the s-v cylinders should fit without filing, being a little smaller. When fitting, set them so that the screw holes are clear of the passageways at each end of the bores. Put the No. 34 drill through the holes in covers, making countersinks on the cylinder flanges. Remove covers, drill the countersinks with No. 43 drill, and tap 6 BA, but don't screw on the covers yet.

The small covers for the ends of the p-v liners are turned from 1.1/8 in. round rod, cast or drawn. Chuck a piece in three-jaw, face, centre, and drill No. 21 to 5/8 in. depth. Turn 5/8 in. length to 1.1/16 in. dia. further reduce 3/8 in. length to 13/16 in. dia. (a tight push fit in the end of the liner), part off at a full 1/8 in. from shoulder, reverse in chuck, take a truing-up skim off the end, and round off the flange. Two of the covers are tapped 3/16 in. × 40 for 3/8 in. depth, to take tail-plugs. These are turned from 3/8 in. round rod. Chuck a piece, turn 7/16 in. length to 3/16 in. dia., round off the end, and part off at 5/16 in. from shoulder. Reverse in chuck, turn $\frac{1}{4}$ in. of the other end to 3/16 in. dia. and screw 3/16 in. × 40. Plugs for both types of cylinder are identical. The covers are prevented from coming out of the liners by a 7 BA countersunk screw running through a No. 41 hole in the liner, into a tapped hole in the cover spigot, as shown in the longitudinal section; a simple job requiring no detailing out.

Flange Plates

Both p-v and s-v cylinders are attached to the engine frames by flange plates, which are made from 1/8 in. plate, either brass or steel being suitable. They are sawn and filed to dimensions and drilled as shown. Note that a small clearance is needed in one bottom corner, to fit over the leading brake-hanger pins in the frame. The drawing of the contact side of the s-v cylinder shows the flange plate attached, 5 BA countersunk screws being used. The plate for the p-v cylinder is

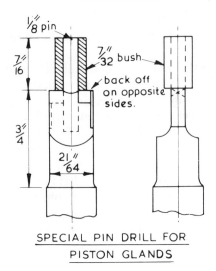

SPECIAL PIN DRILL FOR
PISTON GLANDS

larger, and attached by twelve 6 BA screws. As this plate closes the exhaust way in the contact side of the cylinder, the joint should be steamtight; so true up both the plate and the contact side of the cylinder in the same way as described for truing the s-v portface, and smear the surfaces with either plumbers' jointing or a liquid jointing such as used in automobile work, before screwing up "for keeps."

The pistons and piston-rods for both piston-valve and slide valve cylinders are identical. The piston-rods should be made from 7/32 in. ground rustless steel, but the drawn variety will do if the former isn't available. Two 3.5/8 in. lengths are required. Chuck in three jaw, face the ends, and put ¼ in. of 7/32 in. × 40 thread on the end of each, using a die in the tailstock holder.

Pistons

These can be turned from 1.3/8 in. drawn bronze rod, cast rod, or from separate castings. If cast material is used, it should be of a different grade to that of the cylinder castings. My late lamented friend Harry Sturla, who for many years ran a foundry business at Waltham Cross, and had a wonderful practical knowledge of metallurgy, always said that like metals working together resulted in uneven wear, and I found it so by experiment. Chuck a piece of rod with about 1.1/8 in. projecting from the chuck jaws; too much overhang on the average small lathe is likely to cause chattering. Turn 1 in. length to 1/64 in. over finished diameter. I find that a narrow-ended roundnose tool with about the same amount of top rake as used for turning steel, gives best results when turning hard bronze, and I always use cutting oil, despite the text-book dictum that non-ferrous metals should be turned dry. Experience teaches! Face the end, centre, and drill to 1 in. depth with 3/16 in. or No. 21 drill.

With a parting-tool cut a groove 3/16 in. wide and same depth, at 1/8 in. from the end. Part off at 7/16 in. from the end, then repeat process. Parting-tool chatter which worries beginners and inexperienced workers, can be avoided by running at slow speed and using cutting oil. Chuck each blank in the three-jaw, level with the ends of the jaws, so that it runs truly. Open out the hole with a No. 3 drill for 3/16 in. depth, and tap the remainder 7/32 in. × 40. Put one of the piston-rods in the tailstock chuck, gripping it tightly to prevent slip. Run up the tailstock until the screwed end of the piston-rod enters the hole in the piston and engages the tapped part, then pull the lathe belt by hand until the plain part of the rod immediately behind the screwed part, is drawn into the opened-out section of the hole in the piston. The screwed part of the piston-rod should just be showing through the other side of the piston. This combination of "screw-and-plain" is the surest way of getting an accurate fit. The chucks on Myford and other precision lathes are fitted thus, a fact which speaks for itself.

Finishing

The pistons are finished to size on their own rods, and to ensure absolute concentricity, the rod must be chucked truly. If your lathe has collets, this is simplicity itself; just put the rod in a 7/32 in. collet with the piston close up to it. If not, make a split bush to hold the rods truly in the three-jaw chuck, same as described for holding the steel when turning crankpins. Then grind up the tool

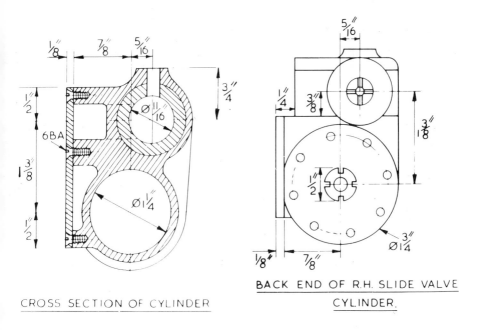

CROSS SECTION OF CYLINDER

BACK END OF R.H. SLIDE VALVE CYLINDER.

used for turning the blanks, and turn the pistons until they are an exact sliding fit in the cylinder bores. Don't worry how much time is taken on this job; if you only fit one in a whole evening it is worth it. The final cuts should be mere scrapes, so that the piston slides into the cylinder bore without a vestige of shake. Use the self-act, if the lathe has one, with the finest available feed. If not, the top slide must be set to turn parallel, as previously described.

It has been stated, and written, that piston fits need not be as exact as all that, because the packing prevents any steam from blowing past. Don't believe it! The packing should merely act as a seal, and not relied on to withstand pressure. During my lifelong experience I have done a lot of overhauling and rebuilding jobs. In several cases when taking a slack-fitting piston out of a cylinder I have found no packing at all in the groove. Under the combination of pressure and friction, the packing had disintegrated, and the tiny fragments had escaped between the rim of the piston and the cylinder bore, making a final exit with the exhaust steam up the blastpipe. Pistons should fit steamtight but not mechanically tight. A good test for a slide-valve cylinder is to put on the front cover, and put the piston in the back end of the cylinder, piston and bore being perfectly dry. Put your thumb over the front port, and up-end the cylinder. If the piston stays put in that position, but falls down to the end of the cylinder if you remove your thumb from the port, the fit is O.K. To apply this test to a piston-valve cylinder, it would be necessary to push a cork into the liner, to cover the port, as you can't very well put your thumb in the liner.

Face off any fragment of piston-rod projecting through the piston, and take a skim over the end of the piston to ensure a flush face. Before removing from collet or bush, try a piece of 3/16 in. square braided graphited yarn in the groove. This should fit nicely at the sides, and stand just a weeny bit above the rim, so that when the piston is in the cylinder, it acts like a piston-ring and presses slightly against the bore. I find that this type of packing varies in size, and if it won't fit in the groove, it is easy enough to enlarge the groove to suit, while the lot is still chucked.

Piston-valves

If the reamer used for reaming the liners is true to size, and has left a hole exactly 11/16 in. dia. then a piece of 11/16 in. ground rustless steel should be an exact sliding fit in it, and all doubts and fears of any beginner about the fit of the valve in the liner, will be dispelled at one fell swoop. All that is needed is to chuck the steel with about 1.$\frac{3}{4}$ in. projecting from the jaws. Face the end, centre, and drill to about 1.5/8 in. depth with 7/32 in. drill. If the drill leaves a burr around the hole, face it off, then put the centre-point in the tailstock barrel, and bring up the tailstock to support the steel whilst reducing the centre part of the valve. Using the same tool as for turning pistons, starting at 5/16 in. from the end, reduce the steel to 7/16 in. dia. for 15/16 in. length. The length of the gap must be no more, no less. What I do, is to set the prongs at the back of my slide-gauge (used for measuring internal diameters) to the required dimension, and turn the gap until they are a tight fit in it. Part off at 5/16 in. from the end of the gap.

Next, chuck the valve in the three-jaw with one end projecting about 3/32 in. Set your slide-gauge to 9/32 in. and take a skim off the end of the valve, so that the slide-gauge fits tightly over the width of the bobbin. Reverse in chuck and repeat operation on the other end. Both ends should be very slightly chamfered, giving the valve a small exhaust clearance, same as I always specify for the cavities in slide-valves. Don't chamfer the inner edges of the bobbins, just leave them sharp, otherwise steam will be admitted too early.

During the latter part of the Kaiser's war (1914-1918) I was in charge of a small munition shop producing aero-engine components, and my experience of reamers was that the commercial variety were more Ananias than George Washington, the holes they left being a little plus or minus their reputed size. I don't support the present-day variety have the reputation of Mrs. Caesar, either, so if you find that the specimen used for reaming the liners has cut over or under size, the valves must be turned to fit. There is nothing to alarm the veriest tyro in tackling this job.

A piece of rustless steel or drawn phosphor-bronze rod will be needed, $\frac{3}{4}$ in. dia. and about 4 in. long. Chuck with 1.$\frac{3}{4}$ in. projecting, turn 1.5/8 in. length to 1/64 in. over finished diameter, then proceed exactly as described above, but don't part right off. Just put the parting-tool in about 1/16 in. Then with the tool used for finish-turning the pistons, proceed exactly as described for turning the pistons to fit the cylinder bores. When the valve is an exact sliding fit in the liner, part it right off, repeat operation, then finish off the two valves to correct length as per previous instructions.

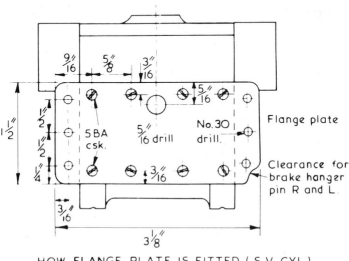

HOW FLANGE PLATE IS FITTED (S.V. CYL.)

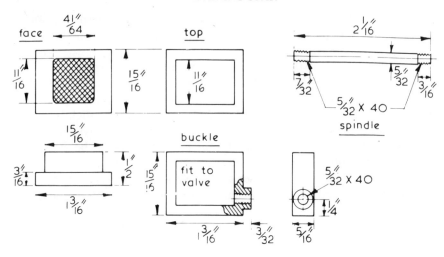

SLIDE-VALVE AND BUCKLE

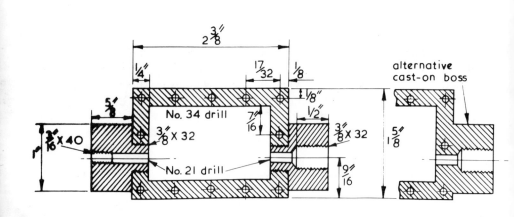

STEAM CHEST AND COVER (SLIDE VALVE CYLINDER)

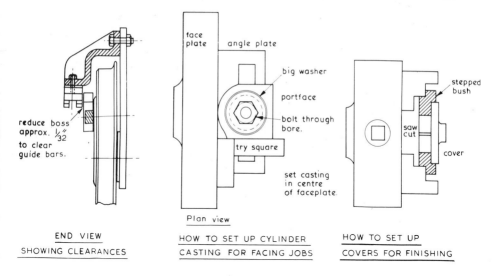

END VIEW
SHOWING CLEARANCES

HOW TO SET UP CYLINDER
CASTING FOR FACING JOBS

HOW TO SET UP
COVERS FOR FINISHING

Valve Spindles

Two 3.5/8 in. lengths of 5/32 in. rustless steel rod will be needed for the valve spindles. The ground variety is best, but drawn rod can be used, also drawn phosphor bronze. Chuck in the three-jaw, put 3/16 in. of 5/32 in. × 40 thread on the one end, reverse in chuck, and screw 3/16 in. of the other end same pitch. For the locknuts, chuck a piece of 5/16 in. hexagon rod; rustless steel is best, but bronze, or brass, can be used at a pinch. Face, centre, drill about $\frac{3}{4}$ in. deep with No. 30 drill, tap 5/32 in. × 40, and part off 1/8 in. slices. Repeat operation when you get to the end of the hole. Don't drill a hole deep enough for all the nuts at one go, because it is a safe bet that the drill will run out of truth at the end, and you can't tap the full depth, anyway, without risking disaster. I put these little tips in to save trouble for beginners, and beg the indulgence of experienced readers.

The nuts require chamfering, so chuck a short bit of $\frac{1}{4}$ in. rod, turn 1/8 in, length to 5/32 in. dia., screw it 5/32 in. × 40, put each nut on it, and with a square-nose tool ground off at one corner chamfer the corners of the hexagon and skim off any burr at the sides. If the sides aren't true, the nuts won't lock properly, and if they come loose when the engine is running, it's going to be just too bad!

Slide-valves

Slide-valves are more trouble to make than piston-valves, when they have to be cut from the solid, but if our advertisers supply castings for both valves and buckles, as they probably will, much of the work is simplified. I used cast valves and buckles on my Southern 2-6-2 (the engine designed at Ashford Works, but never built, owing to British Railways taking over) and they required no machining; just cleaning up with a file. They are usually cast in one unit, to simplify moulding. Saw them apart, then clean up the steps around the tops of the valves with a file. Check the dimensions of the cavity; this is cast under-size, so that the edges can be clean-cut to exact width, a job easily done with a chisel, holding the valve by the step in the bench vice. Tip: when filing the end of the valve, leave it a little over specified length. Then if any slight error is made in the valve gear, the valve can be made to suit, and everything in the garden will be lovely—a direct contradiction of the well-known saying that "two wrongs don't make a right!" The valves can be truly faced by first rubbing them on a big flat file laid on the bench, and finishing on a piece of fine emery cloth laid on something dead flat, as described for the port faces.

Fitting the Buckles

Smooth off the outsides of the buckles with a file, true up what will be the underside by rubbing on a file as mentioned above, then carefully file out the inside of the rectangle so that it is an easy fit on the valve. It mustn't be tight, or the valve will do what the enginemen call "stick up," that is, jam in the buckle, allowing steam to get underneath it and blow straight out of the exhaust. At the same time, it mustn't be slack or the steam distribution will be upset, and the engine will give syncopated beats. Aim for the happy medium; the important thing is, to avoid perceptible end-play. The hole in the boss must also be drilled and tapped dead square with the sides, so that the buckle is true with the valve spindle. If it tilts ever so slightly, it will lift the valve off the portface, and steam will blow straight to the exhaust port. Make a centrepop in the middle of the boss, and set the buckle vertically in a machine-vice on the drilling-machine table, by aid of a try-square. Drill it No. 30, then put a 5/32 in. × 40 taper tap in the drill chuck, enter it into the hole, and turn the chuck by hand until the tap shows through on the inside of the buckle. Then release both chuck and machine-vice, put the buckle with the tap still in it in the bench vice, and finish the job by hand.

An alternative way is to chuck the buckle in the four-jaw with the boss running truly; face, centre, drill No. 30 and tap with the tap in the tailstock chuck. The valve spindles can then be fitted; they are just 2.1/8 in. lengths of 5/32 in. rustless steel or bronze, screwed for 3/16 in. length at each end as shown.

Chassis, with smokebox saddle fitted (N Sturgess)

Front end of chassis and pony truck (photograph by N Sturgess)

CHAPTER SEVEN

The valves

The valves can be cut from the solid, using 1 in. × $\frac{1}{2}$ in. drawn bronze bar. Chuck a piece in the four-jaw, and part off two 1.3/16 in. lengths. Mill the steps to the given dimensions by the same process as described for the pony axleboxes, holding the blank in a machine-vice bolted to the vertical slide, or clamped under the slide-rest tool-holder, if you haven't a vertical slide. In the latter case, the easiest way to "dig out the hole in the middle" would be to make a deep centrepop right in the middle of the face, put it face up in drilling-machine vice, and drill to $\frac{1}{4}$ in. depth with a $\frac{1}{2}$ in. drill. The hole can then be squared up to the dimensions of the exhaust cavity by aid of a $\frac{1}{2}$ in. chisel. I did plenty that way in days gone by. If a vertical slide is available, bolt a small machine-vice to it, put the valve in that, gripping by the steps and go to work just as I described for cutting the ports.

Another trick is to make valves in two parts. In the present case, the bottom of the valve would be a piece of 1 in. × 3/16 in. bronze or gunmetal 1.3/16 in. long with a hole cut in it the size of the exhaust cavity. The upper part would need a piece 15/16 in. × 11/16 in., and 5/16 in. thick. Brass would do for this. The smaller piece is silversoldered over the hole in the larger piece, taking care to keep it central, and no machining is required beyond cleaning off any superfluous silversolder and trimming the width of the valve to given dimensions.

Packing and Jointing

The most satisfactory piston packing that I have so far found is a ring of square braided graphited yarn, with the ends cut at an angle like the joint in a metal piston-ring. This is easy to fit, completely fills the groove in the piston, remains steam-tight for an incredible time (provided that the piston is correctly fitted!) and protects the cylinder bore in the event of a temporary failure in the oil supply. The best mechanical lubricator in the world won't feed if the driver forgets to fill it, and none of us is perfect.

Put the ring of packing in the groove, enter the piston in the bore as far as it will go, then prod all around the packing with a narrow screwdriver, pressing on

the piston at the same time. It will soon slide in! Another wangle which I usually
work with larger pistons is to make a clip from a piece of 1/16 in. brass or steel a
little wider than the piston. This is put over the packing, with the joint in the
packing well away from the gap in the clip, and the bolt tightened until the
packing is squeezed flush with the piston rim. If a blob is sticking out at the gap
in the clip, the bolt is loosened, and the clip turned around a bit so that the blob
is squeezed in when the bolt is tightened again. The bolt is then slackened just
enough to allow the piston to move in the clip, the latter is held against the end
of the cylinder, and the piston pushed out of the clip into the bore. A drop of oil
around the bore makes the transit easy.

The joints between covers and cylinders, and the rectangular joints between
steam-chest, cover and portface, can be made with the rectangular joints
between such as 1/64 in. Hallite, Klingerite, or other well-known brand. For
the covers I just cut out a ring, which fits tightly over the register, avoiding any
ridge or crease, put the cover in position, and poke a scriber down two of the
screw holes to pierce the jointing. The screws are then put in, and the rest of the
screw holes, served in the same way. There is no need to punch the screw holes,
and the screws fit steamtight. Rectangular joints are fitted in similar fashion. If
commercial jointing isn't available, the old-fashioned way of making joints
with thick brown paper, will still do the job. The covers on the ends of the
piston-valve liners need no jointing, as they only have to withstand the exhaust
pressure. The metal-to-metal contact is perfectly sufficient, and even if they did
blow, it wouldn't matter a bean.

Pack the glands with ordinary graphited yarn. This is made up from strands
of yarn twisted into a string about 3/16 in. dia. and must be unravelled for use in
the little glands. Pull out a strand, cut a couple of inches off it, wind a few turns
tightly around the piston-rod or valve spindle, and prod them into the stuffing-
box with a piece of stiff wire, bent at the end. We used similar gadgets made
from 3/16 in. round steel, with one end bent into a ring for giving a better hold,
for packing the glands on full-size engines, and they were known as packing-

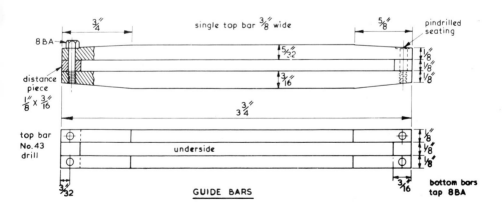

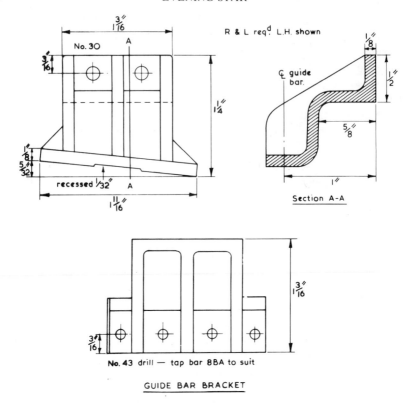

R & L req^d L.H. shown

Section A-A

No. 43 drill — tap bar 8BA to suit

GUIDE BAR BRACKET

shovers. The glands should only be screwed in tight enough to prevent steam leakage, not tight enough to cause unnecessary friction. If too tight, the rods may be damaged; on some of the old L.B. & S.C.R. engines, over-tight pump glands caused the pump rams to assume the appearance of the legs of a navvy's corduroy trousers. The more friction there is to overcome in the "works" of a locomotive, the less power available at the drawbar to pull the load. I have dilated somewhat on the cylinder construction job, for the benefit of beginners, because well-made cylinders are vital to the efficiency of the engine.

On any locomotive with coupled wheels close behind the cylinders, between guide bars and frames, there arises the problem of providing sufficient clearance between crossheads and coupling-rod bosses, without too much reduction in the bearing surfaces. This is quite bad enough on full-sized engines, but on little ones it is just—well, bluepencil, shall we say? We are up against this on the 3.½ in. gauge *Evening Star*; and to complicate matters, she had the Laird type of guide bars and crossheads. I don't like this type at all. The big idea behind it is that the wide solid top bar, plus a crosshead having a bearing surface the full width of the bar, is better able to withstand both thrust and wear on a locomotive which does all its work when running chimney first, as tender engines usually do. For the benefit of the uninitiated, I might explain that the stress all comes on the top bar when running forward, and on the bottom bar when running backward. With the crank on bottom centre, and the piston pushing, the tendency is for the piston-rod and connecting-rod to double up like a pocket-knife on the crosshead pin, forcing the crosshead hard up against the top guide bar. With the crank on top centre and the piston pulling, the latter tries to pull piston-rod and connecting-rod into a straight line, again forcing the crosshead against the top bar. Going backward, the positions are reversed on both centres, and the bottom bar has to stand the racket.

It is obvious that the Laird arrangement is unsuitable for tank engines which have to run with a load in either direction, the bearing surfaces of the two narrow bottom bars being considerably less than that of the wide top bar. Tank engines are therefore usually provided with double guide bars and alligator crossheads, a type which I much prefer, and incidentally is easier to make and erect, especially as it simplifies the clearance problem. However, as the full-size *Evening Star* has Laird guide bars and crossheads, there would be a nice old shindy if I didn't specify them, so I schemed out the arrangement shown. As in full size, the bars are not attached to the cylinders, but are supported by brackets bolted to the frames. These brackets are recessed at the back, to allow clearance for the leading coupled wheels. There is just room for a top guide bar 3/8 in. wide, if the leading coupling-rod bosses are slightly reduced in thickness to allow them to pass. The arrangement is shown in the assembly and erection drawing.

Guide Bars

The best material for the guide-bars is silver-steel, 3/8 in. × 5/32 in. for the top bars, and 1/8 in. × 3/16 in. for the bottom bars. Both are commercial sizes readily obtainable. No machining is needed. Cut two wide lengths and four narrow lengths, allowing a little for trimming the ends, and file to the shape shown. The spaces or distance pieces, are 3/8 in. lengths of the same section steel as used for the bottom bars.

The screw holes in the bottom bars should be absolutely central with the bars, so mark out very carefully their position on the flat side of the bars. For accurate drilling, hold each in a machine-vice with the bar level with the tops of the jaws; and with the machine-vice on the table of the drilling-machine, or held against a drilling pad on the tailstock barrel of the lathe, drill them with No. 51 drill. Next, assemble the bars as shown taking great care to get them in exact alignment. Hold with a clamp at each end. To make sure that the bottom bars are the right distance apart, put a piece of the 1/8 in. silver-steel between them, and hold it while the clamps are tightened. Then using the holes in the bottom bars as guides, drill through the distance pieces and the top bar.

Remove clamps, and mark the bars so that they can be replaced as when being drilled. Tap the holes in the bottom bars 8 BA, open out the holes in the top bar and distance-pieces with No. 43 drill, and slightly pindrill those in the top bar to form seatings for the bolt heads. Don't use ordinary commercial screws threaded right up to the head for holding the bars together; they are liable to break under stress. For jobs like this, I always use silver-steel of the requisite diameter, with a tight-fitting nut for the head. Bolts of this size can also easily be turned from 5/53 in. steel, hexagon preferred. Use one of the distance-pieces to gauge the diameter; it should go on without shake. After assembling, trim off the ends square with the sides, and file the distance-piece flush.

If silver-steel isn't available, mild steel can be used, but the underside of the top bar, and the upper surface of the bottom bars, should be rubbed on a piece of emerycloth laid on something flat and true, such as the lathe bed, to ensure a smooth sliding fit for the crossheads.

Guide Bar Brackets

Castings are available for the guide-bar brackets. Very little machining is required but what there is, must be accurately carried out. The most important thing is to ensure that the part which is bolted to the frame, and that to which the guide bar is attached, must be at right angles, otherwise the crosshead will be all askew, and the connecting-rod won't fit on the main crankpin. Like all other jobs, it is dead easy when you know how! Bolt an angleplate to the faceplate of the lathe, and mount the bracket on it, sloping side down, holding with a clip at each end. Set the back of the bracket at right angles to lathe centres, and take a cut over it with a roundnose tool set crosswise in the slide-rest. Next, clip the faced part to the angleplate, and set the sloping part at right angles to lathe centres. Give that a dose of the same medicine, and the two machined faces will be at right angles. Drill the holes in the brackets as shown.

Crossheads

The crossheads appear tricky to make, but can be built up from mild steel without difficulty, as a three-piece job, body, shoe and arm. The body will need a piece of 3/8 in. × $\frac{3}{4}$ in. section, 1.$\frac{1}{4}$ in. long. One end of this is slotted $\frac{1}{4}$ in. wide, to a depth of 5/8 in. full. The job can be done by any of the methods I have previously described for slotting. If a milling machine is available, grip the piece end-up in a machine-vice on the table, and run it under a $\frac{1}{4}$ in. side-and-face cutter on the arbor. In the lathe, bolt the machine-vice to the saddle, put the cutter on an arbor between centres, and adjust the height of the steel in the vice, to get the correct depth of slot. Three or four cuts can be taken if necessary, at different heights. The machine-vice can also be bolted to an angleplate on the vertical slide, which gives height adjustment, allowing regulation of depth of cut. The method used for grooving axleboxes with an endmill or slot drill could also be tried, but several traverses would be needed to get the required depth.

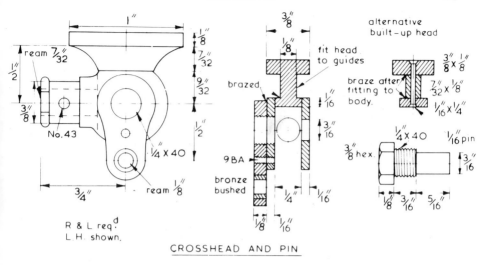

CROSSHEAD AND PIN

To turn and drill the boss, the slotted blank has to be chucked truly in the four-jaw with the solid end outwards. This may cause some beginners to puzzle their heads, but the solution is simple. What I do, is just to jam a bit of $\frac{1}{4}$ in. × $\frac{3}{4}$ in. steel or brass in the slot, parallel with the solid end, and solder it. The slotted end can then be gripped in the four-jaw, and the jaws adjusted until the tip of a pointed tool in the slide-rest just touches all four corners of the projecting blank end when the mandrel is turned by hand. Tighten the chuck jaws, turn the boss to the shape shown, face the end, centre, and drill No. 4 until the drill starts to penetrate the bit of metal soldered into the slot. Put a 7/32 in. parallel reamer in as far as it will go.

Remove from chuck, scribe a line along the middle of one side, and centrepop it at $\frac{3}{4}$ in. from the end of the boss. From the centrepop, strike a circle with the divider points 3/8 in. apart. Drill a 5/32 in. hole from the centrepop, right across the slotted end, making sure it goes through square with the sides; then melt out the bit of packing, and round off the end to the scribed circle. Finally, file a flat at the top of the rounded part, 9/32 in. above the centre of the hole, and clean off all traces of solder.

The Shoe

This can be made from a 1 in. length of $\frac{1}{2}$ in. × 3/8 in. steel. On the wide side, at 1/8 in. from one end, mill a groove 7/32 in. wide and 1/8 in. deep. Turn it over and repeat operation on the other side, leaving a 1/8 in. web between the grooves. Then mill away the bottom to $\frac{1}{4}$ in. wide and 1/16 in. thick. Alternatively the shoe could be built up, the top being a 1 in. length of 3/8 in. × 1/8 in. steel, the web 7/32 in. × 1/8 in. and the bottom 1/16 in. × $\frac{1}{4}$ in. Assemble the three pieces in the form of a T as shown, holding them tightly together with a clamp at each end. Drill a couple of 1/16 in. holes through the middle of the assembly, countersink them, and put in pieces of 1/16 in. iron wire, riveting over both ends.

The crosshead arm, or drop arm as enginemen usually call it, is filed up from a bit of 1/8 in. steel. I save my frame offcuts for jobs of this sort. Drill the holes 5/32 in. for the start, then attach the arm to the side of the crosshead body by a 9 BA screw, lining it up with a piece of 5/32 in. rod put through the holes in crosshead arm and body. Set the shoe in the slot as shown, making sure that it is parallel with the boss. Remove the lining-up rod, and braze the joints at one heat. Just coat them with wet flux (Boron compo mixed to a paste with water is as good as anything) heat to bright red, touch each joint with a bit of thin brass wire, about 16 or 18 gauge, and a little bit will melt off and penetrate each joint. Be sparing with it. If the built-up shoe is used, the joints in that should be done as well. Sifbronze can be used instead of brass wire, if preferred; so can coarse-grade silversolder. When the redness has died away, quench the cross-heads in clean cold water, clean them up, and carefully file away any traces of brass from the grooves, and from the inside of the recess.

Put a 3/16 in. drill through the hole in crosshead and arm. Open out the hole in the arm, and the side of crosshead to which it is attached, with 7/32 in. drill and tap $\frac{1}{4}$ in. × 40. File off the head of the 9 B.A. screw, open out the hole at the bottom of the arm with 3/16 in. drill, and squeeze in a bronze bush. Don't forget that the crosshead should be right and left-handed! Owing to the limited clearance between crosshead and coupling rod, there must be no projection of the crosshead pin on the inside, so a special kind of pin, with the screwed part next to the head, must be used. Chuck a piece of 3/8 in. hexagon steel in the three-jaw, face the end, turn $\frac{1}{2}$ in. length to $\frac{1}{4}$ in. dia., further reduce 5/16 in. of the end to 3/16 in. dia. and screw the remnant of the $\frac{1}{4}$ in. section $\frac{1}{4}$ in. × 40. Part off at 1/8 in. from the shoulder, reverse in chuck, and chamfer the corners of the hexagon head.

Connecting-rods

If a milling machine is available, the table of which has longitudinal movement of not less than 8 in., the method described for milling coupling-rods can be used for the connecting-rods, except for a variation in the way of holding the blanks. If held direct in the machine vice on the table, the overhang at each end would be excessive, and the pressure of the cutter would spring the rods, or perhaps bend them. What I do, is to cut the lengths of steel for the rods about 1.$\frac{1}{2}$ in. longer than specified, allowing for $\frac{3}{4}$ in. overlap at each end. Instead of holding them direct in the machine-vice, they are laid on a piece of 1 in. square steel bar, with a stout clip at each end to prevent any shifting under cut. The bar is gripped tightly in the machine-vice, and the overhang at each end doesn't then matter as the bar is stiff enough to stand up against the thrust of the cutter.

As the connecting-rods have a slight taper, the supporting bar must be slightly tilted in the vice, so that the marked-out line of the connecting-rod is horizontal. This is only about a minute's work.

Put your scribing-block on the miller table and set the needle level with one end of the marked line, then shift it to the other end, and carefully adjust the bar until that end of the marked line is level with the needle point. Check the first end again to make certain that it hasn't shifted, then tighten up the vice and go ahead with the milling.

The recessing is done with each rod clamped down separately on the supporting bar. For the fluting the big end of the rod blank is set slightly to one side, so that the cutter will run parallel to the side of the tapered rod. Use a cutter 3/64 in. away from the side of the rod. Reset the rod on the supporting bar so that the cutter will follow the other edge of the tapered rod, and take a second cut same distance from the edge and same depth as the first one. The result should be a perfect tapered flute. As a matter of fact, it wouldn't be noticeable if the flute is the same width at both ends, in which case one traverse with a 7/32 cutter would do the trick, or the fluting may be omitted altogether—it doesn't affect the working of the engine though it might offend Inspector Meticulous!

Very few if indeed any home-workshop lathes have slide-rests with a cross-traverse of 8 in. so if the milling is done in the lathe as described for the coupling-rods, it will have to be a two-stage job. This entails exceedingly careful setting up on the second stage, so that the cut lines up with the first one. Personally I don't think it is worth the trouble, and would prefer to cut away the surplus metal with a hacksaw, holding the blanks in the bench vice and using the tops of the jaws to guide the saw blade. It is easy enough to saw along the full width of the vice-jaws, and then shift the blanks along so that the cut can be continued. A spot of careful filing afterwards would remove the saw marks.

The ends of the rods can be rounded off in the same way as the coupling-rod

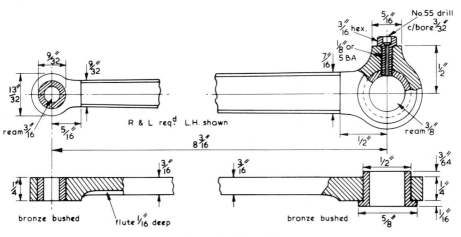

CONNECTING RODS

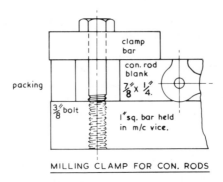

MILLING CLAMP FOR CON. RODS

bosses after sawing off the overlaps. The little ends are bronze-bushed, the bushes being flush with the sides, like those in the middle of the coupling-rod. The big-end has a flanged bush, like the one at the trailing end of the coupling rod, but made to the dimensions given.

Note that it projects through 3/64 in. and forms a distance-piece between the coupling-rod boss and the big-end. The projection which represents the full-size oil box is drilled No. 40, tapped 5 B.A. and furnished with a hexagon-headed brass screw, drilled through No. 55, the head being counterbored 3/32 in. This screw runs right into the big-end bush as shown.

Assembly and Erection

The position of the cylinders is shown on the frame drawing in dotted lines. Put one of the cylinders in position shown, and hold it temporarily in place with a big clamp over cylinder and frame. Put a No. 30 drill into those of the flange holes that are directly accessible, and run it right through the frame plate. Put the end of a bent scriber into those you can't get the drill into, and mark little circles on the frame. Remove cylinder, centrepop the middle of each little circle, and drill No. 30. Replace cylinder, and fix it temporarily with a couple of 5 B.A. bolts.

Remove one of the distance-pieces from a guide-bar assembly, slide the left-hand crosshead into it, replace distance-piece, and make sure the crosshead slides freely from end to end. Put the little end of the left-hand connecting-rod into the crosshead, and secure it with the crosshead pin. Put the big-end on the driving crankpin, hold the crosshead level with the piston-rod of the left-hand cylinder, and turn the wheels until the crankpin is on front dead centre; the piston-rod should enter the crosshead boss, and the crosshead should push in the piston-rod until the piston hits the front cover.

Next, put the left-hand bracket on the top guide bar at 11/16 in. from the end of the bar. Temporarily clamp the bracket to both frame and bar, then turn the wheels and see if the crosshead slides freely from end to end, with no hard spots or binding of either crosshead or piston-rod. If there should be any, adjust the

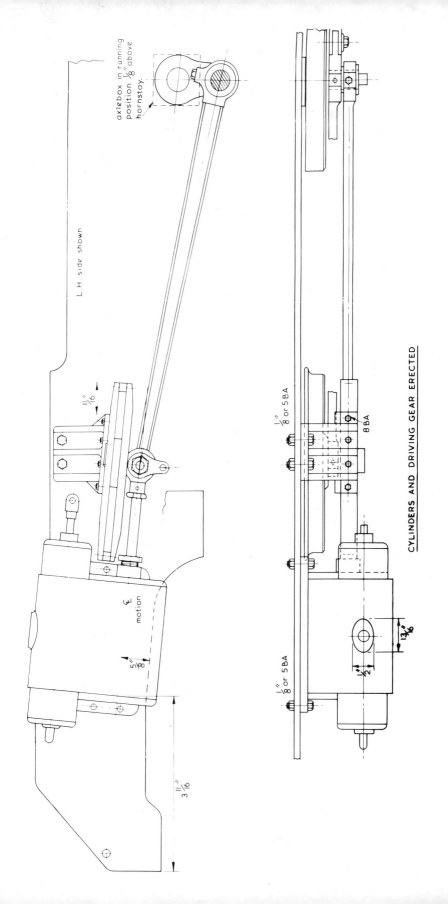

axlebox in running position $\frac{1}{8}$" above hornstay.

L.H. side shown

$\frac{11}{16}$"

motion

$\frac{5}{8}$"

$3\frac{11}{16}$"

$\frac{1}{8}$" or 5 BA

8 BA

$\frac{1}{8}$" or 5 BA

$1\frac{3}{16}$"

$\frac{1}{2}$"

CYLINDERS AND DRIVING GEAR ERECTED

bracket until they disappear. When the required freedom is obtained, the bracket is set O.K. Run a No. 43 drill through the holes in the bracket where it rests on the bar, and make countersinks. Drill the frame No. 50 using the holes in the back of the brackets as guides. Remove bracket, drill the countersinks in the bar with No. 51 drill, tap 8 B.A. and file off any burring, then fix the bar to the bracket with four 8 B.A. screws, hexagon heads for preference. Fix bracket to frame with two 5 B.A. Bolts.

Take off the front cylinder cover, set the crank on front dead centre, and gently tap the piston until it is just 1/16 in. from the end of the bore. This will give 1/32 in. clearance between piston and cover at each end of the stroke. Drill a No. 43 hole through crosshead boss and piston rod, and squeeze in a piece of 3/32 in. silver-steel, which should project about 3/32 in. each side. Replace cylinder cover, and repeat operations for the right-hand side, after which the wheels should turn and the whole bag of tricks work sweetly with no tight places anywhere.

CHAPTER EIGHT

Valve gear

We now come to the job of making and erecting the valve gear; and in my long experience this seems to be the pons asinorum of not only beginners in locomotive construction but quite a number of more experienced workers as well. I don't see any reason why this should be. There is no "witch-doctory" business about valve gears, as some folk would have us believe. Their function is simply (a) to operate the valve so that it admits steam to the cylinder at the point where it can exert its pressure on the piston at the instant the crank passes the dead centre; (b) to cut off steam at any desired point in the stroke; (c) to release the spent steam by the time the piston has reached this end of its stroke, avoiding back pressure on the return stroke; (d) to reverse the movement of the engine. Over 150 different types of valve gears have been devised, some simple, some with weird and wonderful arrangements of rods and links; but of all the lot, the most extensively used have been the Stephenson link motion, and the Walschaerts radial gear. After those, the Joy radial gear, especially suitable for inside cylinders, and the American Baker gear, have been very popular. I have fitted many types of valve gears on the engines built during the past 60 years and more, so should know both good points and faults, and have found that simple gears are the best.

The valve gear on *Evening Star* is the simple straightforward Walschaerts. It differs from the usual arrangement by having the reversing shaft directly operated by the reversing screw, instead of the screw being in the cab and connected to the gear by a long reach rod. The wheel in the cab, which is parallel with the cab side, turns a shaft like the propeller shaft of a motor-car, having a universal joint at each end, that at the front-end being directly connected to the reversing screw. The latter is carried in an upward extension of the bracket carrying the expansion link on the left-hand side of the engine. On the full-size job these brackets are fabricated, and I have had to simplify them considerably to make a suitable arrangement for 3.$\frac{1}{2}$ in. gauge; but they look just like those on big sister. One spot of bother was the supporting plate which is bolted to the frame. On the big engine, there is plenty of room for the plate to go between wheel and frame. On the little one there isn't, as you can see by the drawing. I will explain how the small brackets can be built up, but if our advertisers can supply cast brackets—which will need a rather tricky bit of pattern-making—I strongly advise their use, as it will save much work. Some close fitting will be required but there is nothing for the veriest tyro to worry about, as long as instructions are followed.

Lap-and-lead movement

A desirable feature of the Walschaerts gear is the separate operation of the lap-and-lead movement by connection to the crosshead. The acceleration of the movement and rapid reversal of the valve at each end of its travel, ensures a quick release of exhaust steam, and a correspondingly quick opening of the steam port for the return-stroke. You can tell a Walschaerts engine by its snappy exhaust bark; on my little ones it sounds like pulling a cork out of a bottle, when starting a tidy load. The parts required are valve crosshead, combination lever, and union link. To save unnecessary repetition, please note that all the forked joints in the valve gear can be made in the same way as those in the coupling-rods. Clamp the pieces to be slotted in the slide-rest toolholder, and run them up to a saw-type cutter mounted either on a stub arbor held in the chuck, or a longer arbor mounted between lathe centres. While a cutter the width of the required slot is desirable it isn't essential, as a narrow cutter will cut any width of slot by taking two or more bites. Run the lathe at low speed, and use plenty of cutting oil.

For the valve crossheads, take a piece of $\frac{1}{4}$ in. $\times$ 5/16 in. mild steel about 2 in. long. At about 3/32 in. from each end, starting from the narrower side, drill a No. 32 hole right through the thickness, making sure that it goes through dead square. Next, slot each end as mentioned above, to a depth of $\frac{1}{4}$ in. beyond the centre of each hole. Saw off each end about $\frac{1}{4}$ in. past the end of the slot. Chuck truly in the four-jaw with the sawn end outwards, turn down to 7/32 in. dia. until within 1/16 in. of the slot, then face off the end until the turned boss is 3/32 in. long. Centre, drill No. 30, and tap 5/32 × 40. Finally, round off the slotted ends by judicious use of a fine file, and put a 1/8 in. parallel reamer through the holes.

Combination Lever and Union Link

Each combination lever will need a piece of $\frac{1}{4}$ in. $\times$ 3/16 in. mild steel 3 in. long. Mark off one piece as shown, drill the holes No. 32, use the drilled one as a jig to drill the other, then temporarily rivet them together with bits of 1/8 in. wire, and mill the sides to outline given, by any of the methods I gave for milling coupling rods. Knock out the rivets, and take 1/32 in. off each side of each lever, bringing the thickness down to 1/8 in. below the second hole. This can be done by clamping the lever to a supporting bar, as described for recessing the coupling-rods, and running it under a small diameter cutter on lathe or milling-machine. Saw off the superfluous metal at each end, round off the

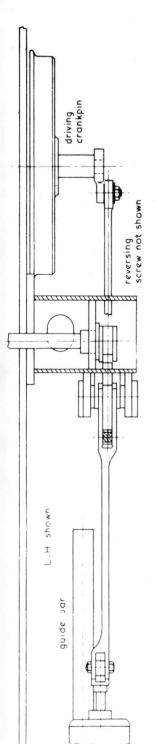

driving crankpin

reversing screw not shown

L.H. shown

guide bar

PLAN OF VALVE GEAR

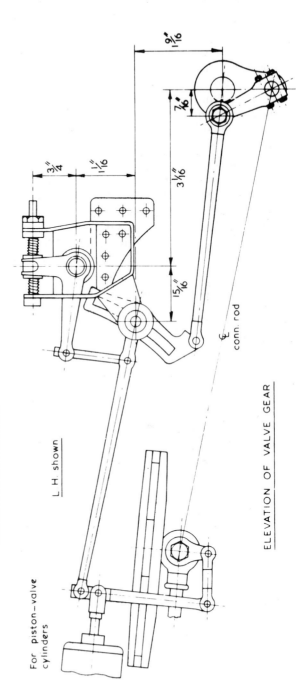

L H. shown

For piston-valve cylinders

conn. rod

ELEVATION OF VALVE GEAR

bottom eye, file the top to outline shown, and ream the holes 1/8 in. The top of the full-size lever is hollowed out to form an oil box, but this isn't needed on the small engine, just drill a No. 55 hole down the top, and countersink it.

To reduce wear to minimum, the holes should be case-hardened. Heat the bosses to bright red, and plunge them into hardening powder, so that the holes are filled with it. Any good make is suitable, such as "Kasenit," "Pearlite," "Ecosite," and so on, sold in small tins at most engineers' supply stores. Repeat the heating and plunging, so that the hardening material penetrates well, then reheat until the yellow in the flame dies away, and plunge into clean cold water. Brush away any traces of hardening material, making sure that nothing is left in the holes, and clean up the bosses with fine emery cloth. They should be so hard that a file will not cut them. If all the pin holes in the valve gear are case-hardened, and silver-steel pins used, it will be a very long time indeed before any slackness develops, and the valve setting will remain accurate.

The union links are made from $1.\frac{1}{4}$ in. lengths of $\frac{1}{4}$ in. $\times$ 1/8 in. mild steel. Mark out carefully, then drill the holes No. 32. It is always advisable to drill the pin holes in small forked joints before the slots are cut, as it ensures absolute alignment. If drilled after slotting, it frequently happens that the drill "wanders," and the holes will not only be out of line, but one will be bigger than the other. They can be milled to outline by aid of the side teeth of a small-diameter endmill held in the chuck, but anybody handy with a file will find it much quicker to file them to the shape shown. Ream the holes 1/8 in. dia.

Radius Rod and Lifting Link

A piece of $\frac{1}{2}$ in. $\times$ $\frac{1}{4}$ in. mild steel $5.\frac{1}{2}$ in. long will be needed for each radius rod. Mark off as shown taking great care to get the offsets right. Then drill the holes and cut the slots; use No. 30 drill for all three holes. Although the slots are offset there is no difference between the right and left-hand sides, as the R.H. rod will fit the L.H. side if turned over, and vice-versa. The rods can be milled to shape by any of the methods desired for the coupling-rods, clamping to a supporting bar with a clamp at each end, when milling the sides. When one side is done, and the rod turned over, only one end will rest on the supporting bar when the rod is set level for milling the opposite side; so put a suitable strip of packing between rod and supporting bar, and clamp the rod down tightly to it. Beginners note that all work to be milled needs to be fixed so that there is no chance of it shifting while the job is in progress. The push exerted by even a small milling-cutter is far greater than they would imagine.

After milling to shape, ream the hole in the short fork only; those in the long fork are left as drilled, as the pins at that end are press-fitted. The superfluous metal at each end can then be sawn off, and the ends rounded as shown.

The lifting link is a simple job, being just a piece of 5/16 in. $\times$ 3/16 in. mild steel $1.\frac{3}{4}$ in. long, milled or filed to the outline shown. Note the projection at the side of the bottom boss. This holds the oil box for lubricating the lifting pin on

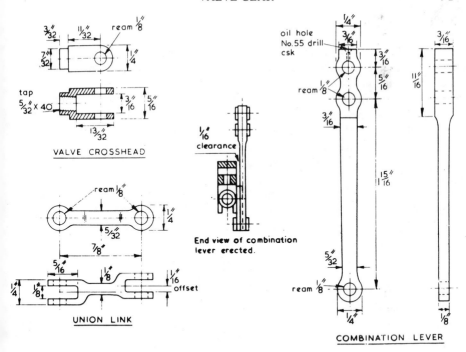

VALVE CROSSHEAD

UNION LINK

End view of combination lever erected.

COMBINATION LEVER

the full-sized engine, and if it isn't present on the little one, our old friend Inspector Meticulous will be getting his note-book out. Drill a No. 55 counter-sunk oil hole in it, also in the top projection, reaming the pin holes last of all.

Expansion Links

Careful work is required to make the expansion links; the job isn't difficult, but requires patience. They are the most vital part of the valve gear, and if they aren't right the valve setting will be incorrect and the efficiency of the engine will suffer. The best material for the links is the fine grade of cast steel used in gauge and tool making, known in the trade as "ground flat stock." I always use it. If mild steel is used, it must be case-hardened to avoid slackness developing between the die-block and link slot. Cast steel links can be hardened right out and last indefinitely. The die-blocks must also be hardened.

Each link will need a piece of steel 2.½ in. long ¾ in. wide and 3/16 in. thick. Coat with marking-out fluid and be mighty careful to mark out correctly. Cut the curved slot first. If a beginner makes an apple-pie of it, he can easily make another start on a fresh piece of metal; but if he gets the outline right, and then messes up the slot, there will probably be a few words to add to the dictionary of railroad Esperanto, besides waste of precious time. The slot can be milled out. Very many years ago I described a special gadget to guide the link while milling the slot with an endmill in the chuck and was amused to see it recently resurrected by somebody else—truly, there's nothing new under the sun! However, it isn't worth the trouble of making it for just two links, when the slots can be cut by hand in a quarter of the time. Just drill a series of 5/32 in. holes as close together as possible, along the centre-line of the slot. File away the metal between the holes with a rat-tail file, then finish to outline with a small fish-back file, or a half-round file will do. Use a bit of 3/16 in. round silver-steel as a gauge, and use the file very carefully until the steel will slide easily from end to end of the slot, without appreciable shake. Anybody with the average amount of care and patience can do the job perfectly, and in less time than might be imagined; you can take that as gospel from one who has done the job scores of times.

About 3/32 in. at each end, the slot should be made slightly over width, so that there is no chance of the dieblock forming a minute step at each end of its extremes of movement; but that job can be done when the block is made and fitted to the link. File the link to given outline, then drill the hole in the tail for the pin with No. 32 drill; use No. 55 for the oil hole, counterboring it with No. 32, and ream the pin hole 1/8 in. The die-block can then be sawn and filed from a bit of the same kind of steel as used for the link, drilled No. 32 and reamed 1/8 in. The hole must go through dead square. After the ends of the slot have been slightly relieved as mentioned above, the block should slide easily from end to end, without the slightest sign of shake, and can then be hardened.

The trunnion blocks at either side of the link can be made from mild steel, 1/8 in. thick. Offcuts from the frame would do. Some close work is called for here, but there is nothing to cause beginners any anxiety. Saw two pieces about $\frac{3}{4}$ in. square, and mark one off to the outline of the trunnion block, shown attached to the link. Drill the hole for the trunnion pin with No. 23 drill, and the rivet holes with No. 53. Use the drilled piece as a jig to drill the trunnion hole in the second piece, but don't drill the rivet holes in it. Put a bit of 5/32 in. rod in the trunnion holes, to keep the pieces of metal in line while you file them both to shape at one fell swoop.

One side of each trunnion block has to be cut away 1/16 in. to a depth of 3/8 in. Hold the block in a machine-vice on the miller table or lathe saddle, and run it under a side-and-face cutter; adjust so that the cutter is 1/16 in. from the edge of the block. If no cutter is available, the block can be made in two parts, each 1/16 in. thick. One part is made to the shape of the block. The other piece, which forms a spacer between block and link, is as shown to the right of the dotted line in the same illustration. Another way is to turn the trunnion-pin and block in one piece from 7/8 in. round mild steel. Chuck a short length, face the end, and turn 3/16 in. length to 3/16 in. dia. Part off at a full 1/8 in. from shoulder. Reverse in chuck, and face the head to exactly 1/8 in. thickness. Coat the side with the pin on it with marking-out fluid; mark out very carefully, locating from the pin and file to outline. Finally cut the rebate.

It is vitally essential that the trunnion blocks are fitted to the links with both pins dead in line, and also in line with the curved slot. They must also be in the middle of the length of the slot. That sounds a tall order, but there is nothing to

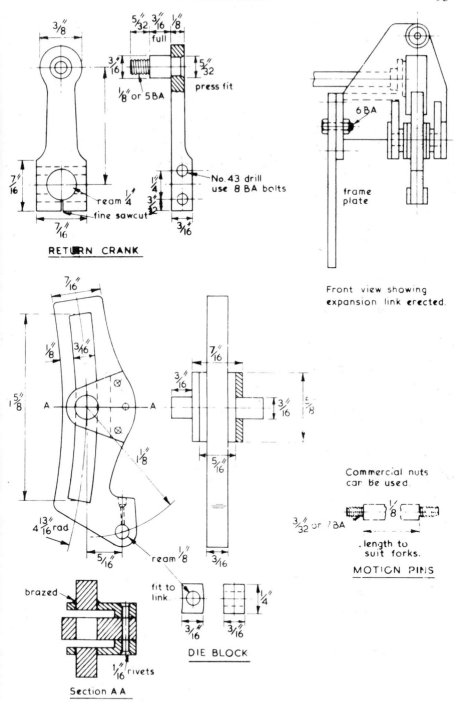

RETURN CRANK

Front view showing
expansion link erected.

Commercial nuts
can be used.

length to
suit forks.

MOTION PINS

DIE BLOCK

Section A A

EXPANSION LINK

it if the job is carried out in the same way as I do it. Open out the pin holes in the trunnion blocks with No. 13 drill, which is 3/16 in. driving fit size, and slightly countersink the holes on the outside of the blocks. Chuck a piece of 3/16 in. round silver-steel, face the end, slightly chamfer it just sufficiently to take off the sharp edge. Part off at a full 13/16 in. from the end, reverse in chuck and chamfer the other end likewise. Squeeze this through one of the trunnion blocks from the countersunk side, until there is only 3/16 in. left projecting. Poke the rod through the slot in the link, and squeeze the other trunnion block on the other side of the link, keeping the two blocks in line. If the trunnion blocks have milled rebates, the wide end of each should now be hard up against the side of the link. If two-piece trunnion blocks are used, put the spacers between the larger pieces and the link.

Adjust the blocks until the pin is exactly in the middle of the slot, and the blocks are in the position shown. Clamp the lot tightly with a toolmaker's clamp, run a No. 53 drill through the rivet holes already in one trunnion block, and carry on right through the link and the other block. Slightly countersink the holes, and rivet the lot together, using pieces of 1/16 in. round steel for rivets; hammer the ends tightly into the countersinks, and file flush as shown in the section. Next—watch your step here—cut out the unwanted middle part of the pin by putting a thin hacksaw down the space between link and trunnion block, filing the cut part smooth on the inside of the block with a thin file such as used by key cutters.

The final job is to braze the pins, and that is easy. Put a smear of wet flux around each pin. Bend up two 3/16 in. rings of 1/32 brass wire, and put one over each pin, close to the trunnion block in the flux. Lay them on some broken-up coke in a small tray (a large tin lid would do) heat until the brass wire melts and flows into the countersinks, which it will do at a bright red heat, then before the redness has all died away, plunge into clean cold water. This will harden both links and pins, and wear will be negligible. If mild steel is used for

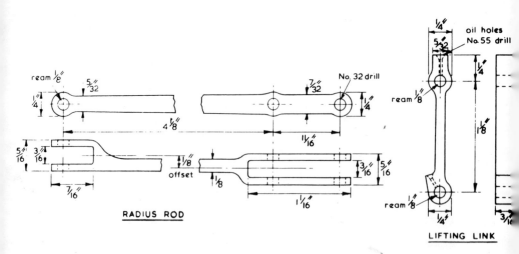

RADIUS ROD

LIFTING LINK

the links, they should be heated and rolled in case-hardened powder, but not quenched before the trunnion blocks are fitted. Scrape off any traces of burnt flux, and clean up with fine emery cloth or similar abrasive.

No brazing will, of course, be needed if the pins are turned solid with the blocks, but great care must be taken to have the pins in line before riveting the trunnions to the links. After clamping the trunnions to the link, test by setting a couple of vee-blocks 7/16 in. apart, lined up to a steel rule. If the link is exactly vertical with the trunnion pins resting in the vees, the pins are in line. See that the clamp is tight before drilling the rivet holes—if anything shifts you've had it!

On the full-size engine, the brackets carrying the expansion links and reversing screw are fabricated, the parts being assembled on a jig, and the parts welded. This cannot be done on the little one, the parts being too small to be held in a jig, and without it the bits would come unstuck. I therefore had to scheme out a simpler arrangement, the pieces of which could be brazed together at one heat. Even this requires care and patience, so if castings are available for both brackets I strongly recommend their use, as much work will be saved. However, for those good folk who would prefer to build up the brackets the following instructions show how the job can be done.

Each bracket consists of a side plate, bracket frame, two lugs for carrying the expansion link bearings, and an angle plate in which the bush for the weight-shaft, or reversing shaft, is fitted. The side plates for both right and left-hand brackets are identical, and are made from pieces of mild steel plate, 1.$\frac{3}{4}$ in. long, 1.1/8 in. wide and 1/8 in. thick. Mark one out as shown, drill the screwholes, use it as a jig to drill the second one, then temporarily rivet the pieces together and saw and file to outline.

The Bracket Frames

These are made from 1/16 in. sheet steel. The left-hand one needs a piece approximately 5 in. long, the right-hand one 2.$\frac{1}{2}$ long, both 1-13/16 in. wide. The upper part of the left-hand bracket is cut to the shape shown, but leave the top overlength. Drill the hole for the front bush $\frac{1}{4}$ in. and the back one 3/8 in. being careful to have them both in line. The 1 in. × 1/8 in. clearance hole for the expansion link must be exactly in line with the hole for the bush. Both bushes should be made from steel rod, as there is a risk of melting bronze or gunmetal when brazing up the bracket. The front bush has a 1/16 in. step turned on it, to fit tightly into the hole in the bracket; the back one is just a $\frac{1}{4}$ in. slice of 3/8 in. round rod with a $\frac{1}{4}$ in. × 40 tapped hole through it.

The lugs for carrying the expansion link bearings are sawn and filed from 1/8 in. mild steel, all four being similar. To hold them in position during the brazing operation, mark out their location on the front of each bracket, and drill a No. 51 hole right in the middle of each marked space. Hold the lug in position, and poke the end of a bent scriber through the hole, to make a mark on the end of the lug where it butts up against the bracket. Centrepop the mark, drill it No.

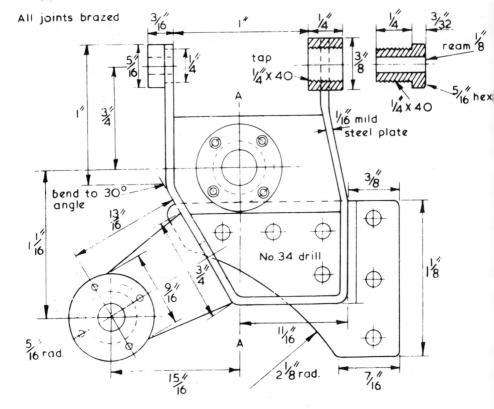

L.H. EXPANSION LINK BRACKET

55, and tap 10 B.A. A steel screw to match will hold the lug to the bracket tight enough to prevent shifting while the brazing business is going on. Note—the holes for the bushes should not be drilled full size until after brazing. Drill them 3/16 in. when making the lugs so that they can be lined up with a piece of 3/16 rod when assembling.

Angle Plates

Each angle plate is made from 3/32 in. mild steel. The left-hand one is a full angle, the upper part fitting between the ends of the bracket frame. The vertical part of the right-hand one has a shaped top. The horizontal part of each angle plate is level with the top of the side plate, as shown in the sections. Don't drill the bush holes full size right away. First cut out the pieces of steel, and bend up the angles, which can easily be done in the bench vice, as 3/32 in. mild steel sheet is very ductile. Mark off and centrepop the location of the bush holes, but before drilling, put each angle plate temporarily in position on the bracket, and

check off the centrepops with the centres of the holes in the lugs which will
carry the expansion links. The vertical distance should be 1.1/16 in. and the
horizontal ditto 15/16 in. for both right and left-hand brackets. If O.K. drill
each centrepop 3/16 in.

Assembling and Brazing the Brackets

This job requires care and patience, but isn't so difficult. Incidentally, wasn't it
Job, of Bible history, who was renowned for his patience? Although he never
brazed up a bracket assembly, his good virtue is worth emulation! The difficulty
is, to prevent the parts from shifting while the operation is in progress. In full
size, the jig on which the parts are assembled, securely holds the lot while each
joint is separately welded. What we have to do, is fix up some arrangement to
hold the pieces so that the lot can be done at one go. Ordinary toolmakers'

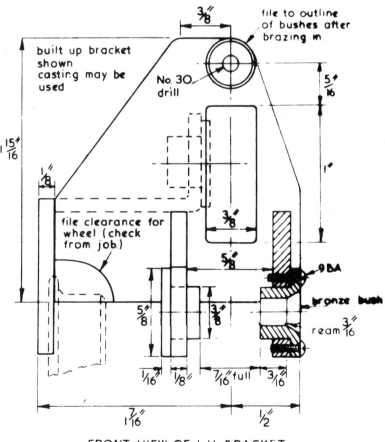

FRONT VIEW OF L.H. BRACKET.

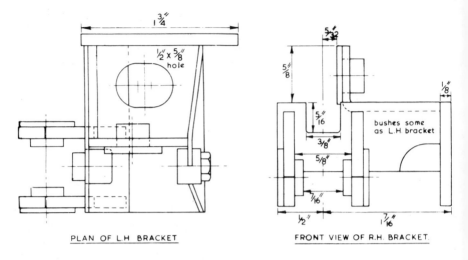

PLAN OF L.H BRACKET   FRONT VIEW OF R.H. BRACKET.

clamps aren't of much use, as they would allow the thin bracket frames to slip, unless screwed up very tightly; and the pressure exerted on the thin metal would cause it to buckle and distort as soon as it became red hot. Besides, the clamps would just about be ruined by the heat of the operation. However, where there's a will there's a way, as the old saw puts it, and the solution is quite simple.

When I have awkward bits to hold in place while brazing or silver-soldering, I usually knock up rough clamps to suit the job in hand. They only take a few minutes, but save endless time and trouble. In the present instance, bend a rough clamp from a bit of 1/8 in. × $\frac{1}{4}$ in. steel rod. Drill and tap one end of it for a 1/8 in. screw. Make a sleeve about $\frac{1}{4}$ in. long, from 5/16 in. round steel, one end of which is drilled No. 30 for about 3/16 in. depth. The other end has a slot milled or filed across it, a full 1/16 in. wide and about 1/8 in. deep. Two will be required to hold the bracket frame securely against the side plate. If the angle plate is made a tight fit between the sides of the bracket frame, it should stay put during the brazing operation; but anybody who is doubtful, can easily make a rough clamp of the ordinary tool-makers' type, from two bits of $\frac{1}{4}$ in. square steel, with 5/32 in. steel screws for adjusting, placed over the vertical part of the angle plate, and the side plate, it will hold them securely without excessive tightening of the screws.

Once the assembly is completed, the brazing operation is simplicity itself. Follow the same procedure as described for the crossheads. Cover the joints with wet flux, lay the whole bag of tricks in a pan of small coke or blacksmiths' breeze, heat to bright red with a blowlamp or gas blowpipe, and touch the joints with a piece of 1/16 in. brass wire, or Sifbronze wire, or other good brand of brazing wire. If the heat is right, the end of the wire will melt and run into the joint like water, leaving a little smooth fillet. Naturally the clamps will become red hot, too, but that doesn't matter an Aswan as long as you don't get any brazing material on them, and stick them to the job. Let the lot cool to black, then quench in clean cold water. Remove the clamps, scrape off any burnt flux that may be sticking to the brackets, and clean up. A flat stick of wood with a wedge-shaped end having a piece of fine emerycloth or similar abrasive glued over the wedge, is very handy for getting into the corners. The upper edges of the left-hand bracket, left overlength for drilling the bush holes and fitting the bushes, can now be trimmed down to the dimensions shown in the front view, the corner is rounded off flush with the bush.

Fitting the Bushes

It is essential that the bushes in which the trunnions of the expansion links work, should be exactly in line, so put a piece of 3/16 in. rod through the holes in the lugs, and check to make sure that it is square with the bracket. If not, correct the holes with a round file, put a $\frac{1}{4}$ in. drill through them, and recheck with a bit of $\frac{1}{4}$ in. rod. When O.K. open them up with a 23/64 in. drill, and put a 3/8 in. parallel reamer through the pair. Check off the position of the hole in the angle plate, and if all right open it out and ream it likewise. Take all the sharp edges off the holes by a touch with a $\frac{1}{4}$ in. drill.

The bushes should be turned from a good hard bronze either cast or drawn. Don't use commercial brass rod, which wears away very quickly. Drawn bronze rod 5/8 in. diameter is available from our advertisers, or from any metal merchants. If cast stick is used it should be $\frac{3}{4}$ in. diameter. Chuck a short length in the three-jaw, and if cast, turn about $\frac{1}{2}$ in. length to 5/8 in. depth using No. 14 drill for the link bushes, and 15/64 drill for the reversing-shaft bushes. For the link bushes, turn down 7/32 in. length to 3/8 in. diameter, a nice push fit in the reamed holes in the lugs. For the reversing-shaft bushes turn similarly, but to $\frac{1}{4}$ in. length. Part off at a full 1/16 in. from the shoulder, reverse in chuck and take a facing skim over the flange to true it up. Countersink the flange side of the

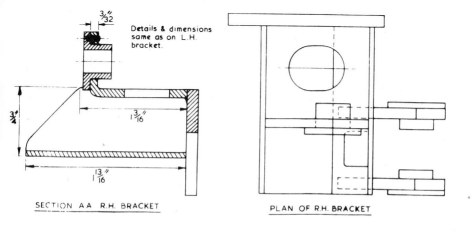

SECTION AA R.H. BRACKET   PLAN OF R.H. BRACKET

link bushes to 3/32 in. depth, either with a big centre-drill, or an ordinary 5/16 in. drill. Put a $\frac{1}{4}$ in. parallel reamer through the reversing-shaft bushes, after facing the flange, holding it in the tailstock chuck.

Drilling the Bush Flanges

To drill the screwholes in the bush flanges, make a jig from a steel washer, same as used for drilling the screwholes in the cylinder covers. Get a washer 5/8 in. diameter, chuck it, and bore out the hole until it just slips over the bushes without shake. Set out the four screw-holes on it, and drill them No. 48.

Put it on each bush, holding it to the flange with a clamp and run the No. 48 drill through the flange, using those in the washer as guides. Countersink the holes in the reversing shaft bushes with No. 21 drill. Put the link bushes in the holes in the lugs, hold with a clamp, run the No. 48 drill through the screwhole, making countersinks on the lugs, follow through with No. 53 drill, tap 9 BA and put round head steel screws in. Ditto repeat with the reversing shaft bushes, but use countersunk screws. Finally, poke a 3/16 in. parallel reamer through each pair of link bushes while they are in place in the bracket, which will make certain that the holes are dead in line. Put a small centre-dot at the top of each flange, so that when removed to insert the links, they can be replaced in exactly the same position.

Erecting Links

If both bushes are removed from the lugs, it will be found quite easy to put the links between the lugs, as the 3/8 in. holes give ample clearance to manipulate them. After inserting, replace the bushes with the holes in them going over the link trunnions, and put in the screws. When these are tightened up, the link should swing quite freely, but without a vestige of shake.

Alternative Cast Brackets

Castings for the link brackets will be the same as the built-up kind, and will require bushing for the link trunnions and reversing-shaft. Not only would it be a very difficult job to cast the bearings integral, needing intricate patterns and cores but the only way to erect the links would be to make one of the lugs removable, entailing extra work. The castings as specified, will need little attention. The side plate which butts against the engine frame, only needs smoothing off with a file. The easiest way to do it is to lay a big flat second-cut file on the bench, and rub the side of the casting on it, taking care to avoid tilting it. The "text-book" way is, of course, to grip the casting in the bench vice, hold the file horizontally, take steady strokes, and so on; but many good folk

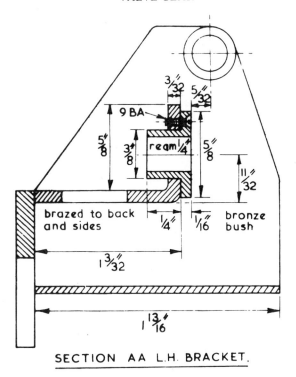

SECTION AA L.H. BRACKET.

wouldn't get a flat face in a month of Sundays by that method, whereas by doing the job as I recommend, they get one at first shot, and in a fraction of the time. Anybody who has a milling-machine can set the casting in a machine-vice on the table, and take a cut over the contact side with a small slabbing cutter; but be mighty careful to avoid distorting the casting when gripping it.

The holes for the screws which attach the bracket to the engine frames should be marked off on the opposite side, centrepopped, and drilled with the contact side resting on a flat piece of wood on the drilling-machine table. Tip: parquet flooring blocks are champion to drill on, being hard wood, and true on both sides. The holes for the link trunnion bushes can be set out on the lugs, as shown in the side views. Drill them 3/16 in. at first, and test with a piece of 3/16 in. rod to see that they line up and are square with the bracket. If not, correct with a round file, redrill $\frac{1}{4}$ in. and test with $\frac{1}{4}$ in. rod. When O.K. open out with 23/64 in. drill, and ream 3/8 in. putting both drill and reamer through both holes at one go.

Next, set out the holes for the reversing-shaft, locating them from the centres of the link trunnion holes. Drill a 3/16 in. pilot-hole first, check to see it hasn't wandered away from the centrepop (drills frequently suffer from wanderlust, especially when the flutes are shallow and the penetrating points wide) then open out and ream as above. Both link trunnion bushes and reversing-shaft bushes are made and fitted exactly as described for the built-up brackets.

The bearings for the reversing-screw will be cast integral with the left-hand bracket. Drill both No. 30; if in correct alignment, the drill, or piece of 1/8 in. round rod (silver-steel is usually perfectly straight, and fine for testing) can be put through both holes, and twisted with your fingers. Open out the back one with 7/32 in. drill, and tap $\frac{1}{4}$ in. × 40. The screwed bush which fits into this, and keeps the reversing-screw in place, is made in exactly the same way as the piston-glands in the cylinders. Use 5/16 in. hexagon bronze, and drill the centre hole No. 30. The bush for the built-up bracket is the same.

Erection of Brackets

The exact position of the brackets on the engine frame is shown in the plan and elevation drawings. The location of the expansion link is the vital factor, so set up the L.H. bracket on the frame, with the centre of the link trunnion bushes in the position shown. Note—a clearance for the intermediate coupled wheel must be filed in the front of the bracket. The curved lower edge of the side plate allows clearance for the wheel flange, but a piece must be taken out of the bracket frame to allow the wheel tread, shown by the dotted lines, to clear. If the bracket is held temporarily against the wheel you can see at a glance exactly what is required.

When the bracket is correctly located, clamp it in place with a toolmakers'

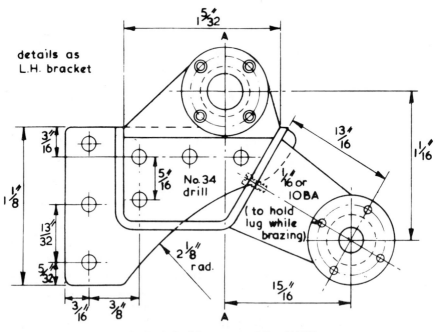

R.H. EXPANSION LINK BRACKET

clamp, check up to make quite sure that the centre of link bearing is the correct amount ahead of the driving axle (clamps do shift sometimes when being tightened!) then drill the engine frame for the bolt holes, using those in the bracket to guide the drill. Don't put all the bolts in yet, as the bracket has to be removed to allow the die-block and radius rod to be attached to the expansion link; just put in a couple of 6 B.A. bolts to hold it for the time being.

The right-hand bracket can then be erected in similar fashion, the link bearing being exactly the same distance ahead of, and above, the centre of the driving axle. After correctly locating the bracket and clamping it temporarily in place for drilling the bolt holes in the engine frame, make an additional check by putting a long straight piece of $\frac{1}{4}$ in. round rod (commercial silver-steel should be straight enough) through the bushes in the two angle plates. This should slide in easily, and should be easy enough to turn with your fingers. If it turns stiffly, or won't go in at all, either one of the brackets is not correctly located, or else the distance between the centres of the bushes for the link trunnion and reversing-shaft isn't the same on both brackets. The remedy for either fault is obvious, and should be put right before proceeding further. Any fault in the valve gear will ruin the efficiency of the engine.

The next item is the reversing screw, and this is made from a 1.7/8 in. length of 3/16 in. round silver-steel. Chuck it in the three-jaw with $\frac{3}{4}$ in. projecting, face the end, and turn down 5/8 in. length to 1/8 in dia. Use the screwed bush from the top of the left-hand expansion-link bracket for a gauge; the turned part should be a nice running fit in the bush, without any slackness. Any slackness in the reverse-screw bearings will cause the whole gear to chatter and dither all the time the engine is at work. Turn the rod end-for-end in the chuck, face the other end, and turn down a full 3/16 in. length to 1/8 in. dia. leaving 1 in. between the shoulders. Grip the longer turned end in the chuck tightly, and screw the unturned part with a 3/16 in. Whitworth left-hand die in the tailstock holder. If a left-hand die isn't available, a right-hand die can be used; but this makes it awkward for the driver.

The reversing wheel on the 2-10-0 engines is mounted parallel with the side of the cab, driving the reversing screw through a bevel gear connected to a revolving shaft with universal joints at each end. With a left-hand screw, to go ahead, the wheel is turned in the same direction that the good lady used to turn the wheel of the domestic wringer, when putting the washing through it, in the days before washing-machines came into general use. This "comes natural" in a manner of speaking. If a right-hand screw is used, the driver has to turn the wheel backwards to go forward (says Pat). This doesn't matter much when the usual type of wheel and screw is fitted, with the whole doings in the cab, and the wheel mounted directly on the end of the screw, at right angles to the cab side. The Stroudley engines on the L.B. and S.C.R. had right-hand screws, which we turned clockwise to notch up, or go into reverse gear; it's just what one gets used to!

To make the nut, chuck a piece of 5/16 in. × 3/8 in. bronze rod truly in the four-jaw. Face the end, turn 1/8 in. length to 1/8 in. dia. and part off at 7/16 in.

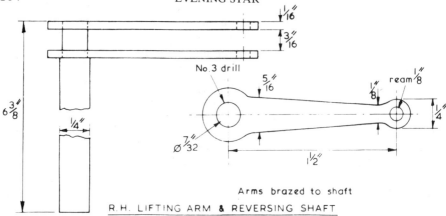

Arms brazed to shaft

R.H. LIFTING ARM & REVERSING SHAFT

from the shoulders. Grip the 1/8 in. pip in the three-jaw, and turn down the other end for 1/8 in. length to 1/8 in. dia. likewise, leaving 5/16 in. between the shoulders. Rechuck the four-jaw with the square end running truly, the pips being at each side. Centre, drill through with 9/64 in. or No. 27 drill, and tap to suit the screw, guiding the tap with the tailstock chuck. The nut should be an exact fit on the thread of the screw, for reasons previously mentioned.

Hold the nut between the lugs on top of the left-hand link bracket, insert the screw through the bush hole, screw it through the nut until the end of the screw enters the front bearing, and screw the bush in place. When the bush is right home, the screw should turn freely, but without any endplay. If tight, take a shade off the front end of the bush, where it bears against the shoulder.

Lifting and Reversing Arms (left-hand side)

Cut two pieces of 16-gauge (1/16 in.) soft mild steel sheet 2 in. long and 1.1/8 in. wide; see that they are quite flat, then solder them together. On one side, mark the outline, drill the holes No. 32, and drill another one at ¾ in. above the location of the bush hole. Saw and file to outline, and cut the slot at the top of the vertical arm by sawing down to the hole—I use a jeweller's thin brass-back saw for jobs like this—and trimming to exact width with a thin flat file. Ream the hole in the small boss with a 1/8 in. parallel reamer. Open the hole in the big boss with 3/8 in. drill. Heat the pieces until they fall apart, and wipe off any solder that may stick to them.

Chuck a piece of ½ in. round mild steel rod, face the end, centre, drill to 3/8 in. depth with letter C or 15/64 in. drill, turn 1/16 in. length to 3/8 in. dia. (a tight fit in the 3/8 in. hole in the arm) part off at 5/16 in. from the end, reverse in chuck, and turn the other end in like manner. Put a ¼ in. parallel reamer in the hole, just far enough to leave the hole a very tight fit on a piece of ¼ in. rod. Squeeze the arms on to the ends of the bush, lining them up exactly by putting a piece of 1/8 in. silver-solder through the holes in the small boss, and a piece of

1/8 in. flat stuff in the slots at the top of the vertical part. Then braze or silversolder the arms to the bush in the manner previously described for other small parts. Quench in cold water and clean up; then very carefully bend the vertical arms outwards until a piece of 3/16 in. square rod will slide nicely between them. The easiest way to get both sides exactly the same, and to the right width, is to file the end of a bit of 5/16 in. square steel rod to the contour shown in the section. First bend the arms outwards at the lower bend, with a pair of flat-nosed pliers; then put the filed end of the 5/16 in. square rod between them, put the lot between the jaws of the bench vice, and tighten the screw. This will squeeze the arms in close contact with the rod without marking them, and as soft mild steel doesn't spring, they will stay put when the vice jaws are released.

Right-hand lifting arms and reversing shaft

The reversing shaft is a piece of $\frac{1}{4}$ in. round steel faced off at each end to a length of 6.3/8 in. Chuck in three-jaw and turn down one end to 7/32 in. dia. for 3/16 in. length. The arms are sawn and filed to the shape shown from two pieces of 1/16 in. soft mild steel 2 in. × 5/8 in. soldered together as before. First drill the holes No. 32, ream the small boss 1/8 in. and open out the holes in the larger boss with No. 3 drill. Press one arm on the reduced end of the shaft tight against the shoulder, and the other just on the end, so that they are 3/16 in. apart. Line them up with a piece of 1/8 in. silver-steel through the holes in the small boss, then braze or silversolder them to the shaft. Quench in cold water, and clean up. Incidentally here is a tip for an extra posh finish, given to me by an ex-instrument-maker, who had a reputation for the excellent finish of his work; use fine-grade emery cloth which has had beeswax rubbed on it.

Return Cranks

Each return crank will require a piece of 7/16 in. × 3/16 in. mild steel, 1.$\frac{1}{2}$ in. long, sawn and filed to the shape shown. Set out and centrepop the location of the holes at 1 in. centres, then drill the hole in the round end with No. 23 drill, and in the squared end with Letter C or 15/64 in. drill. Put a $\frac{1}{4}$ in. parallel reamer in this one, just far enough to make it a very tight fit on the reduced end of the driving crankpin. Slightly recess the back of the crank as shown by milling or filing, and countersink the pin hole.

   To make the crankpin, chuck a piece of 3/16 in. round silver-steel truly, face the end, turn down 5/32 in. length to 1/8 in. dia. and screw 5 B.A. Part off at $\frac{1}{2}$ in. from the end, reverse in chuck and turn 5/32 in. of the other end to 5/32 in. dia. leaving a full 3/16 in. between the shoulders. Squeeze this spigot into the small hole on the flat side of the crank, putting a nut over the thread to protect it; rivet over the end into the countersink, and file flush.

The crank is prevented from turning on the main crankpin, and upsetting the valve timing, by two transverse bolts passing through the thickness of the square end of the crank, cutting through the reduced part of the main crankpin. Make two centrepops on the side of the square end, one at 3/32″ in. from the bottom, and the other at ¼ in. above it, both dead on the centre-line. Put a piece of ¼ in. rod in the hole, grip the crank horizontally in a machine-vice on the drilling-machine table, and drill both holes with No. 43 drill. Plugging the hole will prevent any wandering of the drill, and the grooves left in the plug will be the same as those which will be in the main crankpin when the return crank is fitted. Knock out the plug, and make a cut with a fine hacksaw, from the end of the crank to the hole, which will ensure a firm grip on the main crankpin when the bolts are tightened. The bolts are 5/8 in. lengths of silver-steel screwed 8 B.A. at each end, and furnished with commercial nuts. Silver-steel, by the way, is obtainable in all the B.A. diameters (I keep a small stock of most of them, and find them handy, especially when repinning a worn valve gear) but as an alternative, the holes in the return crank could be drilled No. 41, and 3/32 in. steel used for bolts, with the ends reduced and screwed to take 8 B.A. nuts; anything larger would look clumsy.

Assembling the valve gear

Before the return cranks can be correctly set, and the eccentric-rods made, it will be necessary to assemble and temporarily erect each side of the valve gear. Remove the expansion links from the bearings, put a die-block in the slot at one end, put the long fork of a radius-rod over link and die-block and squeeze a piece of 1/8 in. silver-steel through the holes in the fork and block. File flush at each side, then slide the fork up and down, to make certain that it doesn't foul the trunnion blocks at each side of the expansion link. If it does, a slight touch with a file will soon put matters right. Only what one of my old fellow-conspirators on the L.B. and S.C.R. called "fag-paper clearance" is needed.

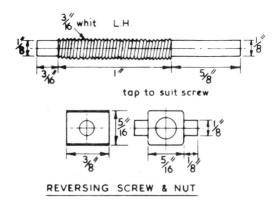

REVERSING SCREW & NUT

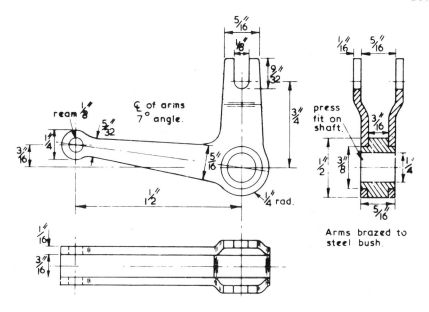

5/16"
1/8"
9/32"
reom 1/8"
€ of arms
7° angle.
5/32"
3/4"
press
fit on
shaft.
1/16" 5/16"
3/16"
1/4"
3/16"
5/16"
1/2"
1/4 rad.
1/2" 3/8"
3/16"
1/4"
5/16"
Arms brazed to
steel bush.
1/16"
3/16"

LIFTING & REVERSING ARMS L.H. SIDE

Connect the other end of the radius rod to the top of the combination lever with one of the special nutted valve-gear pins previously described, then replace the expansion link in its bracket.

Put the combination lever in the jaws of the valve crosshead, line up the holes in the jaws with the hole in the combination lever, and put a pin through the lot. Connect up the bottom of the lever to the crosshead drop arm by aid of the union link, and pin both ends. Set the main crank on bottom centre, and put the return crank on the end of the pin in such a position that it inclines toward the cylinder, the little crankpin on the end approximately 7/16 in. from the centre of the axle.

Now watch your step, for this is really important. Set the main crank on front dead centre, and be sure that it is dead centre, not a scrap above or below. Set the expansion link in such a position that you can run the radius rod and die-block from one end of the slot to the other, without any movement of the valve spindle taking place. The link will then be exactly in mid-movement. Fix it there so that it can't accidentally shift; I usually put a wedge between link and bracket, with a small clamp over the lot. Next, with a pair of dividers take the distance between the centre of the hole in the tail of the link, and the centre of the return crankpin. Now turn the wheels until the main crank is on back dead centre, and apply the divider points to the hole in the link tail and centre of the return crankpin as before. If they tally, it will be just as much a miracle as a golfer holing in one stroke. If they don't, which is far more likely, adjust the return crank until the pin moves half the distance that it is "out", then repeat process. When the distance between centres of hole in link tail and return crankpin tally exactly on both front and back dead centres, the return crank is correctly set, and the distance between the divider points is the exact distance between the centres of the eccentric-rod bush and the pinholes in the fork, so take care to avoid shifting them until the eccentric-rods are made. It's as simple as that!

The return crank can now be fixed in position. Taking great care to avoid moving it in the slightest, put a strong clamp, or hand-vice, or anything else that will grip tightly, over the sides of the square at the end of the return crank, leaving the upper transverse hole clear. Run a No. 43 drill through it so that the drill cuts a groove in the crank pin, as it did in the plug. Put a bolt in, and screw up as tightly as possible without stripping the threads. Remove clamp, drill the other hole and put a bolt in that as well. The crank should then be as firmly fixed as the Rock of Gibraltar, yet it can be instantly removed in case of necessity, and replaced without the slightest trouble in exactly the same position.

Eccentric Rods

Two $4.\frac{1}{2}$ in. lengths of $\frac{1}{2}$ in. × 5/16 in. mild steel will be required for making the eccentric rods. Scribe a line down the middle of the wide side, and make a centrepop on it at 5/16 in. from one end. From this, with the dividers set as mentioned above, strike off the length of the rod, and make another centrepop at the exact point where the line struck by the divider point crosses the centreline—and when I say "exact", I mean just that. The divider points should go plumb into the middle of each centrepop when applied to both at once. On the full-size engine the length between eccentric-rod centres is 5 ft. 3.15/64 in. and when they get down to sixty-fourths in full-size to get correct valve setting, it doesn't need Sherlock Holmes to deduce what is going to happen to the setting on a $3.\frac{1}{2}$ in. gauge job if a 1/64 in. error creeps into that size! By getting the exact length of the rod in the way I described above, all trouble and source of error is avoided.

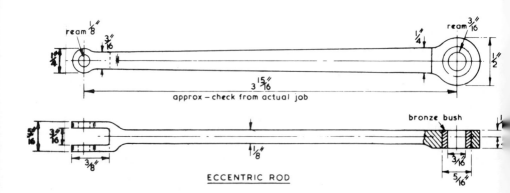

ECCENTRIC ROD

Mark off the outline of the rods as shown and proceed to cut them to shape, drilling, slotting and bushing as described for the other rods in the valve gear. Both right and left-hand rods are the same, although the boss is offset, the rod fits either side by merely turning it over. On the full-size engine, the boss contains a ball bearing. While this isn't absolutely necessary on the little one, as a bronze bush stands up to the job quite well, a ball bearing could be fitted with advantage, if one of the requisite size is available. The outside diameter should be not more than 3/8 or 10mm. and the boss should be bored out to a tight push fit for the bearing. The return crankpin must, of course, be turned to fit the bore of the bearing. As most of the stress of driving the valve gear comes on the return crankpin bearing—and this is considerable when the engine is hopping along at a tidy lick with a heavy load—a ball bearing reduces the friction practically to nil and, as wear is negligible, it should last the lifetime of the engine.

Fitting the reversing shaft

First remove the reversing screw and nut, then put the shaft, with right-hand lifting arms attached, through the bearings in the brackets, from the right-hand side of the engine. Put the left-hand lifting arms through the slot in the front of the L.H. bracket, line up the bush with the shaft, and push the shaft through it, keeping the lifting arms on both sides of the engine in line, as near as you can "by eye". Drop the pins on the sides of the nut, in the slots at the top of the vertical arm, and replace the screw.

Next, put the lifting links in place in the long forks of the radius rods, as shown in the valve gear assembly drawing, then the upper ends can be fitted between the lifting arms and secured by two of the nutted pins. Now turn the reversing screw until the pin in the left-hand die-block is dead in line with the expansion-link trunnions; then take a look at the right-hand side and see if that die-block pin also lines up exactly with the link trunnions. If it doesn't, adjust it until it does, so that both sides move exactly in unison when the reversing screw is turned. When O.K. drill a No. 43 hole through the boss on the left-hand lifting-arm assembly, and squeeze in a piece of 3/32 in. silver-steel, which will effectually prevent any attempt by the right and left-hand lifting arms to get out of line. When the die-blocks are in the middle of the expansion links—that is, mid-gear position, there should be no movement of the radius rods when the wheels are turned by hand. If one rod moves and the other doesn't, the lifting arms have not been correctly lined up, and this should be corrected right away, otherwise the valve-setting will not be the same on both sides of the engine and the beats will be irregular or syncopated.

Front of tender nearly complete (photograph by N Sturgess)

Front end of the tender, showing water pipe (photograph by N Sturgess)

Partly finished tender from rear (photograph by N Sturgess)

*Near side view tender, showing **neat** riveting* (photograph by N Sturgess)

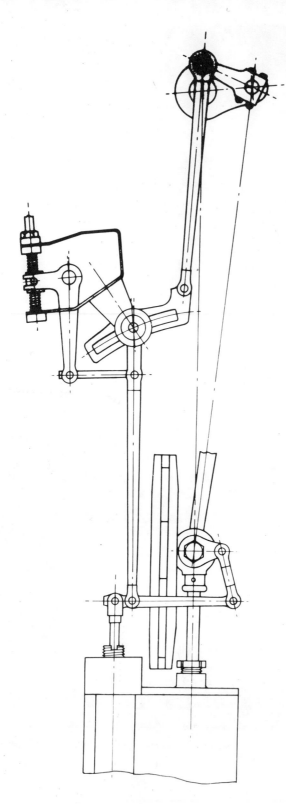

ARRANGEMENT OF VALVE GEAR & SLIDE VALVE CYLINDERS

CHAPTER NINE

Valve gear for slide-valve cylinders

As previously mentioned, the slide-valve cylinders were arranged so that the same layout of valve gear described for the piston-valve cylinders, could be used for operating the slide-valves, by changing over the connections at the top of the combination lever, and setting the return crank to lead the main crank instead of following it. Generally speaking, this is quite correct, as can be seen from the drawing, but there is another factor to be considered, which will necessitate slight variation in the dimensions of some of the parts. Owing to the inclination of the cylinders, and the necessity for keeping the valve gear below the running-boards, the centre of the expansion link is well below the point where the radius rod is connected to the combination lever, and the radius and swing of the expansion links are arranged to suit. When the connection is dropped below the valve-spindle crosshead, the point of connection on the combination lever is brought 1/16 in. nearer to the centre of the expansion link. This means that the radius of the link will be 4.$\frac{3}{4}$ in. instead of 4.13/16 in. all the other dimensions, and the method of construction, remaining the same. No cause for alarm!

Now, if we use the same combination lever, it would have to be lowered 5/16 in. and this would not only mean excessive angularity of the union link, but would affect the vertical distance between the combination lever and the crosshead arm. This is easily got over. Simply reduce the distance between the pinholes at the top of the lever, and shorten the tail end of the lever a proportionate amount, so that the lever has a slightly greater amount of oscillation, and the top of it moves just as much as it did before. The amended dimensions are shown in the drawings, the construction remaining unchanged.

Now take the radius rod. The overall length between the end pin-holes has to be the same as the radius of the expansion link, viz. 4.$\frac{3}{4}$ in. but owing to the lower point of connection to the combination lever, the expansion link will need to tip over a little more at the top, in the direction of the cylinder. To prevent it knocking its head against the lifting link every time it makes its bow, we shall have to shift that merchant a little farther away, 13/16 in. instead of 11/16 in. and lengthen the depth of the forks and the general construction remaining as previously described. The long arms on the reversing shaft at both ends, must also be lengthened to match.

The return crank will also need shortening by 1/16 in. The hole in the link tail is above the centre-line of cylinders and driving axle, increasing the angularity of the centre-line of the eccentric rod, so that the circle swept by the return crankpin cuts it above the cylinder centre-line when the pin is on front dead centre, and below it on back dead centre. With the return crank leading the main crank, the measurement is taken from the centre of the main crankpin on bottom centre, to the back dead centre of the return crankpin, and is approximately as stated. If the return crank is made 15/16 in. between centres, and the exact length of the eccentric-rod obtained as fully described in the preceding paragraphs, the engine will do the job in the approved L.B.S.C. style. Incidentally the original return crank could be used, setting it to follow the main crankpin as with the piston-valve cylinders, in which case the engine would go ahead when the dieblock is in the upper half of the expansion link, same as the Maunsell "mongolipers" (2-6-0) on what used to be the Southern Railway. This would be an advantage if the reversing screw has been made with a right-hand thread, as the engine would then go in the same direction as the reversing wheel is turned.

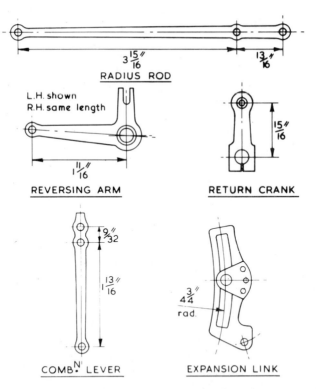

Dimensions not shown are the same as for p.v. cylinder gear.

Variations in valve gear dimensions needed for s.v. cylinders.

Exhaust Pipe Arrangement for Double Chimney

The original design of the class 9 engines called for a single chimney and blastpipe, same as the *Britannias*. However, the good folk at Swindon had been doing some experimenting with double chimneys and blastpipes, with considerable success, so they applied this type to the later class 8's, including *Evening Star*. I have got better results with the single chimney in 3.½ in. gauge size. As I've often remarked, Nature won't be "scaled", and little engines have to be designed to suit the rail gauge. Anyway, to suit the fancy of builders of this engine, I will describe both types—just take your choice!

I mentioned previously that the cylinders should not be permanently erected, but only temporarily with two or three bolts, so take them off, easily done by disconnecting the radius-rod from the combination lever, taking out the screws in the guide-bar bracket, and removing the crosshead pin. This is necessary for the insertion of the screws which hold the exhaust-pipe flanges to the frame. Scribe a circle 5/8 in. dia. around the exhaust hole in the frame, drill three No. 41 holes on it at an equal distance apart, and countersink them.

Exhaust Cross Pipe

The cross pipe, of the "breeches" pattern, is made up from two pieces of 5/16 in. × 20-gauge copper tube. Bending tip for beginners: to avoid kinking never use pliers to hold pipes when bending them. My 3.½ in. gauge 4-6-2 has a similar cross pipe, and the way I made it was first to soften the end of a length of tube by heating to red and plunging into clean cold water. A piece of lead wire was then pushed into the tube; a short length of hard tube 5/16 in. bore was put over the softened end, and by holding this in one hand, and the unsoftened end of the 5/16 in. tube in the other, a perfect bend was produced by hand pressure only, without the least sign of kinking. The lead wire was melted out, the bend cut off to the required length, the process repeated, and there were my bends.

I use lead wire to prevent the tube from kinking, as I have a small stock of various diameters purchased umpteen years ago, but it isn't essential. If one end of the tube is plugged, melted lead can be very carefully poured into it and allowed to cool to solidity before bending, or the tube may be filled with fine sand, and plugged at both ends. Beginners will be agreeably surprised to find how easily the tube can be bent, when it is first softened as mentioned above.

After cutting the bends to length, file away half the diameter of each short end. For the flanges, chuck a piece of 7/8 in. round brass rod, face, centre, and drill with letter N or 19/64 in. drill, to a depth of about 3/8 in. Part off a 1/8 in., slice, reface the end, and part off another slice. Ream the holes so that they fit tightly on the ends of the halves of the cross pipe, and squeeze them on with the faced sides outwards. Hold the halves together, and try the assembly in place between the frames, which the flanges should just touch. If O.K. put the assembly in the brazing pan—a bit of thin iron binding-wire will prevent the

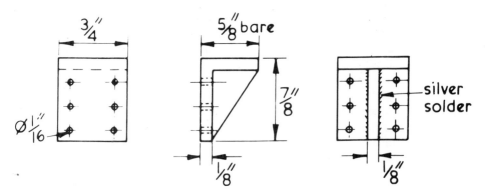

BRACKET FOR REVERSING GEAR : I off brass

joint coming apart—and silversolder the joint and the two flanges at one heating. Pickle, wash off, and clean up, then screw the top of the joint 5/16 in. × 40 for $\frac{1}{4}$ in. down. The same cross pipe does for either a single or double blastpipe.

Put the assembly between the frames, and line up the flanges with the exhaust holes, keeping the screwed top of the pipe vertical. Put a small clamp over frame and flange at each side, to hold it in place; run a No. 41 drill through the three countersunk holes in the frame, making countersinks on the flanges. Follow through with No. 48 drill and tap 7 B.A. As there is only exhaust pressure to withstand, jointing gaskets between frame and flange are not needed. Just remove the cross pipe, and scrape off any burring left by the drilling and tapping, so that both flanges and frames are quite smooth. Replace the pipe and fix it with countersunk screws through frame and flanges. As the pipe is soft, the screws will pull the flanges steamtight against the frames. I usually smear a little liquid jointing, as used in motorcar work, over the contact faces, as an extra precaution.

Double Blastpipe

On the full-size engine, the double blastpipe is a casting with separate nozzles bolted on, and these nozzles have a cored passage into which the blower jets are screwed. It would be very difficult to reproduce this in 3.$\frac{1}{2}$ in. gauge size, so I have devised a much simpler arrangement which is easily made. It is just a piece of tube bent into a U-shape, with turned brass nozzles silversoldered on, and a tapped bore at the bottom for screwing on to the cross pipe. With this arrangement, only a small hole is needed in the bottom of the smokebox, as the blastpipe can be screwed in place after the smokebox is erected. A separate ring blower will be fitted over each nozzle.

The blastpipe is made from a piece of 5/16 in. × 20-gauge copper tube, same as the cross pipe, and is bent to shape by the same method. The "horns" should be 1 in. apart. To make the nozzles, chuck a piece of 7/16 in. round brass rod, face, centre, and drill to about ¾ in. depth with No. 20 drill. Bevel off the end to 5/16 in. dia. for 1/8 in. length, and part off at 5/16 in. from the end. Bevel and part off another similar bit, then chuck each with the larger end outward, and open up the holes with letter N or 5/16 in. drill for 1/8 in. depth. The nozzles should fit tightly on the horns of the blastpipe.

To make the boss, chuck the 7/16 in. rod again, face, centre, and drill to about ½ in. depth with 9/32 in. drill. Part off at 3/8 in. from the end, rechuck, and run a 5/16 in. × 40 tap through. File a half-round groove across one end of the boss, so that it fits closely to the bottom of the blastpipe. Put a bit of binding-wire around it and the blastpipe to keep it in place, then silversolder it and the nozzles at one heat. Pickle, wash off, and clean up, then run the 9/32 in. drill through the boss into the blastpipe. Don't leave any chips inside!

Single Blastpipe

Chuck a piece of ½ in. hexagon brass rod with about 1.½ in. projecting from the chuck jaws. Face the end, centre, and drill to about 1.½ in. depth with No. 3 or 7/32 in. drill. Open out to a depth of 1.1/8 in. with 9/32 in. drill, and tap 5/16 in.

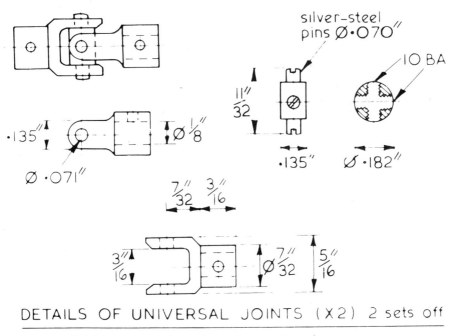

DETAILS OF UNIVERSAL JOINTS (X 2) 2 sets off

B.M.S. case harden jaws & spider

ARRANGEMENT OF REACH ROD

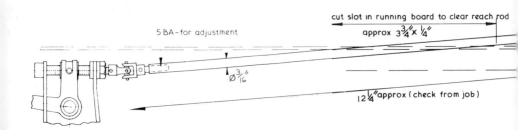

cut slot in running board to clear reach rod

5 BA-for adjustment

approx $3\frac{3}{4}'' \times \frac{1}{4}''$

$\varnothing \frac{3}{16}''$

$12\frac{1}{4}''$ approx (check from job)

dia. and part off at 1.5/16 in. from the end. Reverse in chuck, gripping by the turned part, and bevel off the end of the hexagon to 7/8 in. dia. and 3/16 in. depth. The ring blower will fit over this coned top, when the smokebox is erected and the blastpipe permanently fitted.

How to Set the Valves

After fitting the exhaust cross pipe, the cylinders can be erected "for keeps". See that the contact side of each cylinder is quite clean and smooth, also the frame plate to which it is attached. It is advisable to smear a thin coating of the liquid jointing previously mentioned, over both the contact faces, leaving it to become tacky before putting the cylinder in place. All the fixing bolts can then be put in and tightened up, the guide bars and brackets replaced, and the radius rods reconnected to the combination levers.

I always set piston-valves by air pressure. In the top of the steam-chest there is a 7/32 in. hole for admission of steam. Put a $\frac{1}{4}$ in. × 40 tap into it just far enough to cut about three threads. An inch of copper tube with one end screwed to match, is screwed into this, and connected by a rubber tube to a motor tyre pump. That is all the apparatus needed.

To be able to develop maximum power, there should be full steam pressure on the piston at the instant the crank passes dead centre; and as everything in this benighted world takes time, the valve must of necessity open the steam port a shade, admitting steam before the crank reaches dead centre. For beginners' information, the amount of opening is called "lead". With Walschaerts gear, the lead is constant; that is, the valve "cracks" the port, as the enginemen say, exactly the same amount at each end of the stroke whatever the position of the die-block in the expansion link, and it is the action of the combination lever which attends to that part of the business. Therefore, all we have to do is to set

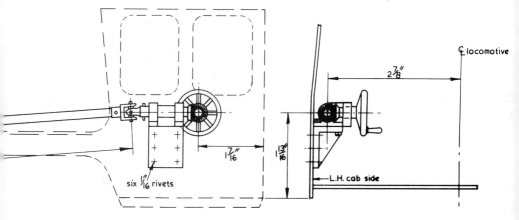

six $\frac{1}{16}''$ rivets $1\frac{7}{16}''$ $1\frac{13}{16}''$ $2\frac{7}{8}''$ ₵ locomotive

L.H. cab side

the die-blocks in the middle of the expansion links, so that the radius rods don't move when the wheels are turned by hand, and adjust the piston-valve on its spindle until it cracks the port an equal amount at each end of the stroke when the crank is on dead centre.

Turn the wheels slowly by hand in the forward direction. They should be raised clear of the bench by putting wood blocks, or anything else handy, under buffer and drag beams. As the crank approaches front dead centre, press on the pump handle, forcing a little air into the cylinder. If the valve is correctly adjusted, there will be a "siss" from the front drain-cock hole as the crank reaches dead centre. However, the chances are, that it will siss either before or after. If before, the port is opening too early, and the valve wants moving back a little on the spindle. If after, the valve is opening too late, the valve needs moving forward. Adjustment is easily made by taking out the pins at the top of the combination lever and pushing the rods clear, removing the back steam-chest cover, and pulling out the valve and spindle. Slack off the locknuts, make the adjustment, then be very careful to tighten the locknuts so that the valve cannot move endwise, but can be twisted easily on the spindle between finger and thumb.

When the front end is O.K. turn the wheels until the crank reaches back dead centre. If the valve is correct to length, the siss will be heard as the centre is reached, and the job is done. All that remains is to give the other cylinder a dose of the same medicine.

Setting Slide-Valves

The slide-valves can be set by the same process, the only difference being, that as steam is admitted at the outer edges of the valve, it will require moving forward if the port opens too early, and back if the opening is late. Adjustment is made by screwing the valve-spindle in or out of the boss of the valve crosshead. The valves can also be set by sight, in which case the steam-chest covers must be removed. With the die-blocks in the middle of the links as before, turn the wheels slowly by hand, and watch the edge of the valve closely. When the crank reaches dead centre, the port should just appear as a thin black line at the edge of the valve. If it appears before or after dead centre, adjust by screwing the spindle into or out of the crosshead as before mentioned. Check back dead centre likewise, and when each port cracks on the dead centre, the setting is O.K. Drill a No. 52 hole through crosshead boss and spindle, and squeeze in a bit of 1/16 in. silver-steel, which will prevent the adjustment being upset.

Tips on Valve Adjustment

None of us being perfect, it sometimes happens that slight error is made in the dimensions of a valve, or the size of a port, which passes unnoticed. When an attempt is made to set the valves, they just won't come right. Maybe one port cracks on dead centre, but the other doesn't, and no amount of adjustment will make both ends behave themselves. However they can soon be taught good manners. Suppose with a piston-valve you get the siss from the drain-cock hole on front D.C. but no amount of adjustment will produce a siss from the back

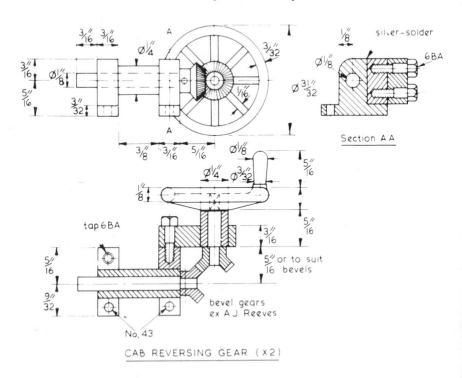

CAB REVERSING GEAR (X2)

hole until the crank has passed back D.C. Well, the trouble is that the distance between the valve bobbins is less than it should be. The remedy is, to take out the valve, and turn a tiny shade off the inner edge of both bobbins. It is useless to reduce one only, as both bobbins must be exactly the same length, if the valve events are to be correct. After reducing, reset the valve on the spindle and try again.

It is a rather more serious matter if the siss is heard correctly on front D.C. and then before the crank reaches back D.C. This indicates that either the inner edges of the steam ports are too close together, or the valve bobbins are a wee bit too far apart. Obviously nothing can be done about the ports, and as the bobbins are solid with the middle part of the valve, they can't be closed in. The quickest way out of the trouble is to make a fresh valve with the bobbins a little closer together, say a bare 15/16 in. between, and make a fresh start with the setting. A bit can always be taken off in places where it can't be put on.

With slide-valves, the opposite obtains. If the front port cracks on D.C. and the back one doesn't crack until the crank has passed D.C. then the valve is too long, and a shade should be filed off both ends, so that the cavity is kept exactly in the middle. If the back port cracks before D.C. then the valve is too short, but unless you happen to be a close relation of Inspector Meticulous, there is no need to make a new valve. Just silver-solder a strip of brass 3/16 in. wide and about 1/32 in. thick, to each end of the valve, letting it project just below the valve face. Trim the ends, and reface the valve. It will then probably be a little too long, but is very easily reduced to correct length by treating as mentioned above.

Finally, never lose any sleep about any variation in the amount of port opening. The only valve gear in the wide world which gives equal port openings at both ends of the cylinder in both directions, is the simple loose eccentric. All full-size engines vary in the port openings, some to a considerable extent, especially in back gear. The vital factor is that each port shall crack on dead centre in either direction of motion; and if they do that, then the engine will do the job in the approved fashion.

Top: *This picture shows the dummy
Wakefield lubricator and drive
from expansion link*
(photograph by H G Lumb)

Top left: *The backhead of Mr
Lumb's model of "Evening Star".
The asbestos lagged pipe leads to an
ashpan cleaning valve*
(photograph by H G Lumb)

Left: *A look inside the smokebox of
Mr Lumb's "Evening Star"*
(photograph by H G Lumb)

Far left: *The dummy vacuum
ejector serves as the blower tube*
(photograph by H G Lumb)

Right: *This view shows the injectors
and some of the pipework*
(photograph by H G Lumb)

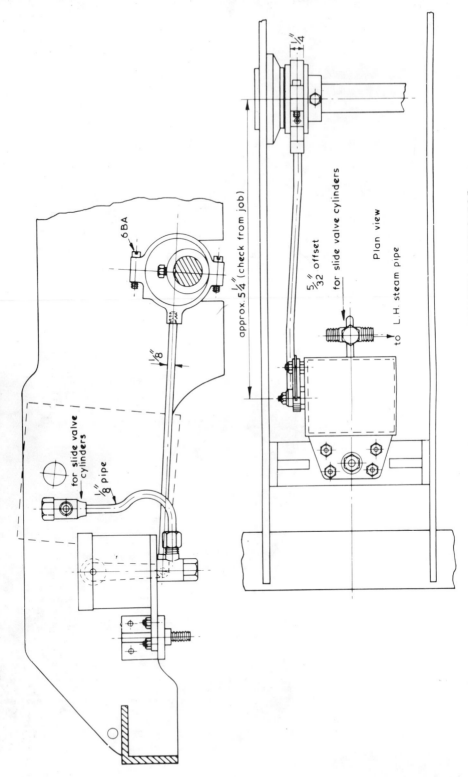

6BA

approx. 5¼" (check from job)

⅛"

for slide valve
cylinders

⅛" pipe

1¼"

5⁄32" offset

for slide valve cylinders

Plan view

to L.H. steam pipe

ARRANGEMENT OF MECHANICAL LUBRICATOR

CHAPTER TEN

Cylinder Lubricator

It is essential that any locomotive using superheated steam in bronze or gunmetal cylinders, must have an adequate and continuous supply of oil, the viscosity of which must enable it to stand the heat without excessive thinning or vaporising. This is provided by a mechanical lubricator, consisting of a tiny pump working inside the oil tank, and driven by a ratchet gear.

The oil tank is made with an extended baseplate which is bolted to the top of the pony bolster, in a position accessible for easy filling. The drive to the ratchet lever is taken direct from an eccentric on the first coupled axle. Oil is delivered via a check valve with two outlets, which will be connected to the steam pipes leading to the cylinders.

The rush of steam picks up the oil and carries it in a fine spray to the valves and pistons, giving perfect lubrication.

Oil Tank

Cut a piece of 18-gauge sheet brass a full 5.½ in. long and 1.¼ in. wide, and bend it into a rectangle measuring 1.½ in. × 1.¼ in. with the joint at one corner. Cut

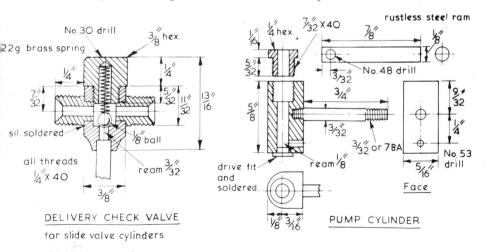

DELIVERY CHECK VALVE
for slide valve cylinders

PUMP CYLINDER

out the baseplate from 13-gauge (3/32 in.) brass to the shape and size shown, but leave the part which forms the tank bottom, a little wider, which makes the silversoldering job easier. Put the base in the brazing pan and stand the tank body on it, smear some wet flux all around the bottom and in the corner joint, heat the lot to medium red, and apply a strip of best-grade silversolder, or Easyflow wire, to the joints. This will run like water if the heat is right, leaving a neat fillet. Pickle, wash, and clean up.

Tips for beginners: bend up the tank over a jig block in the bench vice. The simple gas blowpipe which I described previously is just the gadget for the silver-soldering, as it gives the required heat without risk of melting the thin brass sheet. I use a 2-lb jam jar as pickle bath for these small jobs, and it stands on a shelf at the back of my brazing forge, nice and handy. Keep it about half full, and when not in use, keep a lid on the jar to prevent evaporation.

After cleaning up, file the sides and back of the baseplate flush with the tank, then drill all the holes. The 3/16 in. hole should be right in the middle of the tank bottom, as it locates the pump stand.

Drill another 3/16 in. hole in the centre-line of the right-hand side of the tank, at 3/16 in. from the top, through which the bearing will pass when the pump is assembled. Don't leave any burring. The lid is made from a piece of 18-gauge sheet brass measuring 2 in. × 1.$\frac{3}{4}$ in. Snip a $\frac{1}{2}$ in. square out of each corner, and bend down $\frac{1}{4}$ in. of each side, so that it will just snap on to the tank top. After fitting, silversolder the corners, but only just use the weeniest bit of silversolder, or the lid won't fit. Smooth off any sharp corners.

Oil Pump

Chuck a piece of 5/16 in. square brass rod truly in the four-jaw, face the end, centre, drill to 3/16 in. depth with No. 22 or 5/32 in. drill, and tap 3/16 in. × 40. Part off at 1.$\frac{1}{4}$ in. from the end. At $\frac{1}{4}$ in. from the drilled end, mill or file a recess on one of the facets, 5/16 in. long and 1/16 in. deep. At the other end, mill or file a 1/16 in. rebate $\frac{1}{2}$ in. long, on the same facet. Make a centrepop exactly in the middle of the recess, that is 13/32 in. from the bottom of the stand, and with a pair of dividers with the points set $\frac{1}{4}$ in. apart, strike an arc across the facet below the recess, with one of the divider points in the centrepop. On this arc, at 1/16 in. each side of the centre-line of the stand, make two more centrepops. Warning to beginners—take the greatest possible care to get that bit exactly right, as the efficiency of the oil pump depends on it.

Next, very carefully indeed, drill the right-hand centrepop with a No. 53 drill, until it breaks through into the tapped hole. Avoid forcing the drill, or you'll have another kind of break which will necessitate a visit to the tool stores. Drill the left-hand centrepop to a depth of 1/16 in. only; then, with a little chisel made from a piece of 1/8 in. silver-steel, reduced to 1/16 in. at the end, chip a groove from the hole to the bottom of the stand. The distance between the holes at their inner edges, must be not less than 1/16 in. otherwise the port in the pump cylinder will bridge them, and there will be what our electrical friends call a short circuit. It won't blow any fuse, but will prevent the pump from working properly!

Now drill a No. 41 hole through the stand, from centrepop in the middle of the recess. Turn the stand over, and open out the hole from the other end to a depth of 1/8 in. with a ¼ in. pin drill. Finally, at 3/16 in. from the top of the stand, drill a No. 22 hole, and tap it 3/16 in. × 40. This hole, and the hole in the middle of the recess, must go dead square through the stand, so if you haven't a reasonably accurate drilling machine, use the lathe, with the drill in the three-jaw chuck, and the stand held tightly against a drilling-pad in the tailstock barrel. True up the faces above the recess, by rubbing on a piece of fine emerycloth laid on the lathe bed, or something equally flat and true.

The pump cylinder is made from a piece of 3/16 in. square rod, faced off truly at each end to a length of 5/8 in. Scribe a centre-line across one end, and at 1/8 in. from the edge, make a centrepop. Chuck in four-jaw with this pop mark running truly, drill through with No. 32 drill, and ream 1/8 in. Open out the hole to 5/32 in. depth with 3/16 in. drill, and tap 7/32 in. × 40. Make a little gland to suit, from a piece of ¼ in. hexagon rod, by the same process as the cylinder glands, drilling No. 32 and reaming 1/8 in.

On the facet farthest away from the reamed hole, scribe a line down the middle, and make a centrepop 9/32 in. from the top, with another exactly ¼ in. below it. Drill the first one No. 48, to a bare 1/8 in. depth. Beginners will probably "overshoot the platform" as the enginemen say, and pierce the bore, but it doesn't matter, as the trunnion pin seals the hole, which is tapped 7 B.A. The lower hole is drilled No. 53 into the bore. Both holes must go through dead square, same as those in the stand. Run the 1/8 in. reamer through the bore again, with the gland screwed in place, to clean out any burring and true up the gland, then turn a little plug to fit tightly in the bottom of the bore. This should just reach to the bottom of the port. Squeeze it in, and solder over the head, to make sure oil doesn't force it out. These wee pumps can exert enormous pressure. For curiosity's sake the gauge tester at one of the British Railways locomotive works, tried one on his full-size testing machine and stopped at over 600-lb per sq. in. to avoid straining his master gauge.

The trunnion pin is a 7/8 in. length of 3/32 in. rustless steel (silver-steel will do if rustless isn't available) screwed for 1/8 in. length at one end, and 3/16 in. at the other, to match the tapped hole in the cylinder. True up the portface before screwing it in, and make quite certain that it stands out exactly at right angles to the portface. If it doesn't, the portface won't bed down truly to the rubbing faces on the stand, and oil will come out between them, causing failure of the pump. The pump ram, or plunger, is a 7/8 in. length of 1/8 in. rustless steel, with a No. 48 cross hole drilled 3/32 in. from one end. The gland is packed with a strand of graphited yarn. The spring is wound up from 22-gauge tinned steel wire (piano wire would do) and secured by an ordinary commercial nut. The outside of the cylinder can be rounded off as shown in the plan view, but it isn't essential.

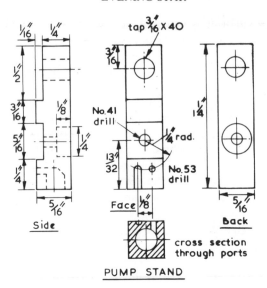

PUMP STAND

THE LUBRICATOR STAND

The crankshaft is a 1.7/16 in. length of 3/32 in. rustless or silver-steel, with 1 in. of 7 B.A. thread at one end, and 5/32 in. ditto at the other. The crank is a 1/8 in. slice of 3/8 in. round rod with a hole in the middle, tapped to suit the shaft. At 1/8 in. from the centre, drill a No. 53 hole, tap it 9 B.A. and screw in a 5/16 in. length of 15-gauge spoke wire, threaded to suit. Wire spokes of various gauges can be obtained from any cycle shop, and the material makes first-class crank-pins, valve-gear pins and so on. As ratchet wheels can be obtained from our advertisers, it is hardly worth while setting up all the apparatus to cut just one. The hole in it will probably be under size, so open it out with No. 43 drill, and squeeze it on to the crankshaft, so that it is $\frac{1}{4}$ in. from the shorter screwed end. Take care to put it on the right way, so that it will ratchet the shaft clockwise.

For the bearing, chuck a length of 5/16 in. hexagon rod, face, centre, and drill to 1 in. depth with No. 41 drill. Turn down 7/8 in. length to 3/16 in. dia. and screw 3/16 in. × 40. Part off at a full 1/16 in. from the shoulder, reverse in chuck, skim truly and chamfer the corners of the hexagon. Make a nut 1/8 in. thick from the same rod, to act as a locknut.

Check Valves

For the check valve under the tank, chuck a bit of 3/8 in. round rod—gunmetal or bronze for preference, but brass will do—face the end, centre, and drill No. 43 for about $\frac{3}{4}$ in. depth. Open out the bottom with 7/32 in. drill and D-bit to 11/32 in. depth, tap $\frac{1}{4}$ in. × 40 for a full 1/8 in. depth, and slightly countersink the end. Part off at a bare 1.1/8 in. from the end, reverse in chuck, turn down 5/32 in. length to 3/16 in. dia. and screw 3/16 × 40. Put a 3/32 in. parallel reamer through the No. 43 hole. Drill a No. 20 hole halfway along the body part, for the union nipple, which is made exactly the same as the nipples on the feed pump and silversoldered in.

The cap is made in the same way also, but the hexagon head is $\frac{1}{4}$ in. long and instead of being solid, it is drilled for the spring which holds the ball in place. Before parting off, centre it and drill to 5/16 in. depth with No. 30 drill. Part off at $\frac{1}{4}$ in. from shoulder, reverse in chuck, and chamfer the corners of the hexagon. The spring can be wound up from 22-gauge hard brass or bronze wire, and must be an easy fit in the hole. Touch the ends against the side of a fast-running grinding wheel, to square them off; a ragged-ended spring will push the ball off the seating instead of holding it in place. Seat a 1/8 in. rustless ball on the end of the reamed hole in the recess, and assemble the lot.

To make the delivery valve, chuck the 3/8 in. rod again, and proceed as described for the one under the tank, but this time part off at 9/16 in. from the end. Reverse in chuck, open out the No. 43 hole with No. 32 drill for about 1/8 in. depth, and bevel off the end. Put the No. 20 drill right through the body part, and fit two union nipples at opposite sides. Fit a 2 in. length of 1/8 in. copper tube into the counterbored end of the valve body, and a $\frac{1}{4}$ in. × 40 union nut and cone on the end of the pipe. I usually make union nuts and cones a dozen or more at a time, and always have some handy. For the nuts, chuck a piece of 5/16 in. hexagon brass rod in the three-jaw, face, centre, and drill No. 30 to the full depth of the drill flutes. Open out to about 3/16 in. depth with 7/32 in. drill, tap $\frac{1}{4}$ in. × 40, and part off at a full $\frac{1}{4}$ in. from the end. Ditto repeat until you come to the end of the No. 30 hole, then re-centre, drill No. 30 again, and carry on until you have about a dozen nuts. Each one can be put separately into the chuck to chamfer the corners of the hexagon.

Make the coned nipples from copper rod. This, being soft, beds into the union cone even if the angles of taper are slightly different, and you never get steam leakage. Chuck a bit of $\frac{1}{4}$ in. copper rod, face, centre, and drill No. 40 for

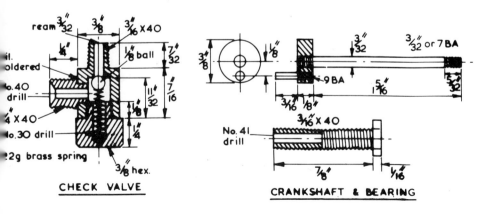

CHECK VALVE　　　　　　　CRANKSHAFT & BEARING

about ½ in. depth. Turn down about 1 in. length to an easy sliding fit in the union
nut, then turn the end to a cone, either with the top slide set over to a 30° angle,
or with a tool which has the cutting edge ground off to the same angle. Part off
at 1/16 in. from the end of the taper. Repeat operation for the number
required. Chuck one with the larger end outwards, and open out the hole for
1/16 in. depth with No. 32 drill, to fit on the 1/8 in. pipe. The two screwed
nipples, and the pipe joint and cone can then be silversoldered at one heat.
Take care to avoid getting any silversolder on the taper of the coned nipple.
Pickle, wash off and clean up, then fit a ball, spring and cap, same as the valve
under the tank.

Ratchet Drive

The ratchet lever is filed up from a piece of 3/32 in. × ¼ in. steel strip, and drilled
as shown. The pawls are filed up from the same material, and drilled No. 41 for
the pivots. The driving pawl has a 1/16 in. hole in its tail for the spring.
Caseharden both pawls as described for valve-gear parts. The driving pawl is
attached to the lever by a 3/32 in. screw with 3/32 in. of "plain" under the head,
and must be perfectly free to oscillate without side shake. The check pawl is
mounted on a stud turned from a bit of 3/16 in. steel rod one end of which is
turned to fit the hole in the pawl, and screwed for a retaining nut. The other end
is turned down and screwed 8 B.A., put through a No. 43 hole drilled in the
tank, and is nutted inside. The pawl is kept in contact with the teeth of the wheel
by a 19-gauge wire spring, bent as shown, and attached to the tank by an 8 B.A.
screw nutted inside the tank.

Assembly and Erection

Attach the pump cylinder to the stand, put the latter in the tank, and screw the
check valve into it through the hole in the baseplate. Put the bearing through
the hole in the side of tank, put on the locknut, and screw the end of the bearing
into the tapped hole in the top of stand. It must not be tight enough to pull the
stand out of place, but merely support it; then tighten the locknut against side
of tank, and tighten check valve, so that the union on it points backwards. Hold
the crank disc in position with the crankpin through the hole in the pump ram,
and push the shaft through the bearing, screwing it into the crank disc. When
tight, the shaft should be quite free to turn, having just a shade of endplay. Then
put on the ratchet lever, setting the pawl against the teeth of the wheel, and
secure it with a nut and washer. This should be free to oscillate, without any side
rock. Finally connect the tail of the pawl to the hole in ratchet lever by a
30-gauge wire spring.

    To test, put some motor oil in the tank, and turn the ratchet wheel until oil
appears at the check valve outlet. Then press your thumb over the outlet as

tightly as possible, and work the ratchet lever. If the pump is O.K. it will be impossible to prevent oil from squeezing past your thumb, no matter how hard you press. If no oil comes out, it will be escaping between pump cylinder and stand, and the retaining spring will need tightening up a little.

To erect the lubricator, temporarily clamp the baseplate extension to the top of the pony bolster, and run a No. 41 drill through the holes, making counter-sinks on the bolster. Remove lubricator, drill the countersinks No. 48, tap 7 B.A., countersink the tapped holes on the underside of the bolster, and put screws in, about 3/8 in. long. Put the baseplate over the projecting screws, and secure with nuts. Bend the pipe attached to the delivery valve to the shape shown, and connect up the union nut to the screwed nipple under the oil tank.

The eccentric strap is machined and fitted exactly as described for the feed pump eccentric strap. The rod is made from a 4.3/8 in. length of 1/8 in. steel rod, one end of which is screwed into the lug on the strap, and other end furnished with a little fork, made in the same way as those in the valve gear. This is attached to the ratchet lever by a pin made from 15-gauge spoke wire, screwed 9 B.A. at each end and nutted. Be sure to have all the parts working quite freely but without slackness. The ratchet lever should click one tooth of the wheel, at every revolution of the coupled axle.

Steam Brakes

Working brake gear on small locomotives is useless for stopping purposes. Any full-size driver will confirm that although the engine pulls the train, it is the brakes on the coaches that do the best part of the stopping. Although *Evening Star* is very heavy, the momentum of even a couple of passengers on an eight-wheeled car travelling at slow speed, would cause her to slide on the rails with locked wheels if the engine brakes were applied with any force. It is therefore necessary to fit brake gear to the car, and let the load on it provide the stopping power, having brake gear on the engine merely for the sake of appearance. As a matter of fact, the brake gear could be dummy, just consisting of the brake-blocks and hangers, the latter being fixed so that the blocks just kept clear of the wheel treads; but if there is one thing I detest more than another, it is fitting dummy gadgets on a little locomotive when they can be easily made to operate. For that reason I am specifying working steam brakes, which can be easily made and fitted.

The arrangement shown in the drawings is similar to that which I fitted to my 4-6-2, which works perfectly. The cylinder and its supports differ a little from those on the full-size engine, which couldn't be reproduced as a working proposition in 3.½ in. gauge. For example, the full-size cylinder is a fixture, and to allow for the movement of the end of the actuating lever on the brake shaft, the piston-rod is hollow, with a little connecting rod inside it, the upper end of which is attached to a gudgeon-pin, like the arrangement on a petrol engine. To reproduce this in 3.½ in. gauge would be about as useful for working purposes as

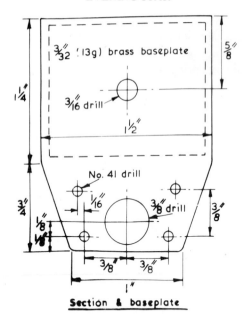

Section & baseplate

putting wrist-watch works in a grandfather clock. The cylinder shown, being
supported on trunnions carried in a substantial triangular bracket, allows for
the "arc" end-movement of the long brake lever. The whole of the actuating
gear is a single self-contained unit, easily detachable in case of necessity.

Brake-blocks and Hangers

I mentioned in the introduction that the brake fitting was going to be a pretty
tight squeeze, and it will need care and patience, but there is nothing to scare
even a raw tyro. The brake hangers are filed or milled from 1/8 in. × ¼ in. mild
steel, or offcuts of frame steel could be used. The ends should be rounded off as
described for valve-gear components. The hanger supports are turned from ¼
in. round mild steel in the three-jaw chuck. Turn down 9/32 in. length to 1/8 in.
dia. and screw 5 B.A., leaving about 3/32 in. of "plain" next to the shoulder.
Part off at 7/8 in. from the end, reverse in chuck, turn down 9/32 in. of the other
end, so as to leave 5/16 in. between the shoulders, slip one end of the hanger
over the turned end, and run the die on until it just touches the hanger. This
wheeze ensures that when the whole bag of tricks is assembled, and the nut
tightened, the hanger will just be free enough to swing without any side
shake—which is as it should be!

The brake-blocks may either be cast-iron, or cut from steel ¼ in. thick. Pin the
blocks to the hangers with bits of 3/32 in. silver-steel, filing the ends almost
flush. The blocks should be a wee bit stiff on the hangers so that if the brakes are
applied, the blocks should be able to bed down full length on the wheel treads

THE MECHANICAL LUBRICATOR

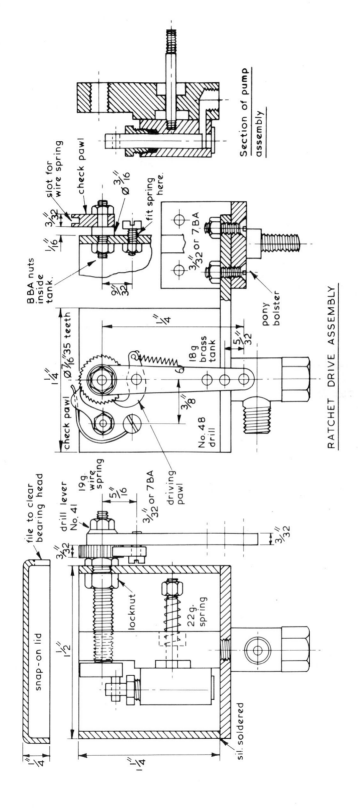

file to clear bearing head

snap-on lid

drill lever No. 41

19 g. wire spring

3/32 or 7 BA

driving pawl

locknut

22 g. spring

sil. soldered

1/4

1/4

1/2

3/32

5/16

3/32

slot for wire spring

check pawl

Ø 3/16

fit spring here.

8 BA nuts inside tank.

3/32

1/16

9/32

3/32 or 7 BA

pony bolster

RATCHET DRIVE ASSEMBLY

check pawl

Ø 1/16 35 teeth

1/4

1/4

18 g. brass tank

5/32

No. 48 drill

3/8

Section of pump assembly

and stay at the same angle when released. They should not be loose enough to lop over and rub one end on the wheel treads when the engine is running. The hanger supports may be attached to the frame and secured by nuts on the inside, but don't fit the hangers permanently until the beams are made.

These are the next job. Four of them are made from ½ in. × 1/8 in. flat steel, the "odd man out" being 7/16 in. wide only and all 4.1/8 in. long. Chuck truly in four jaw, turn ¼ in. length to 1/8 in. dia. and further relieve a bare 1/8 in. length to 3/32 in. dia. screwing 7 B.A. Drill the No. 30 holes and file to shape, then fit the hangers on one side of the engine, and put on the nuts. Poke one end of the beams through the bottom holes—don't forget that the narrow one leads—put on the other hangers, and nut up the lot. When all the nuts are tight, each pair of hangers should be just free to move without being the least bit slack. Such close quarters makes good fitting essential, though there is nothing difficult about the job.

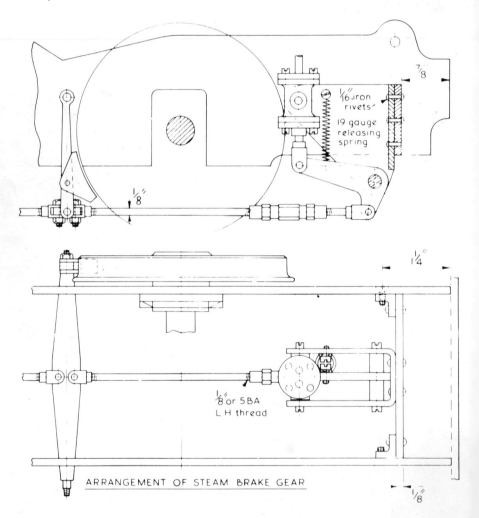

ARRANGEMENT OF STEAM BRAKE GEAR

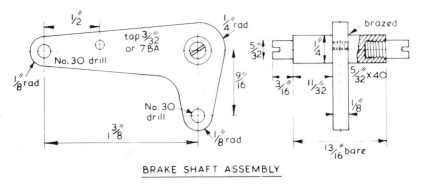

BRAKE SHAFT ASSEMBLY

Brake Cylinder

The brake cylinder will probably be cast solid, as it isn't worth while coring such a little hole. Chuck the casting in the four-jaw with one end running truly; two of the jaws should grip on the side bosses, and the other two holding the flange. Face off the projecting flange, and turn it to ¾ in. dia. Centre, drill right through with 23/64 in. drill,, and ream 3/8 in. To get a clean true bore without any scratches in it, hold the reamer in the tailstock chuck, enter the slightly-tapered end of the reamer in the drilled hole, then grip the tailstock tightly and slide it bodily along the lathe bed, pushing the reamer clean through the casting steadily but non-stop, right to the end of the flutes. Pull it steadily out again, also non-stop, and if the cutting edges of the reamer are O.K. the bore should be as smooth as glass. Beginners' tip: run your finger-nail along the cutting edges of the reamer before operating, and if you feel the slightest roughness, rub it off with the end of your oilstone. The other flange of the casting is turned and faced with the cylinder on a stub mandrel, same as the engine cylinders.

If the casting is now chucked crosswise in the four-jaw with one of the side bosses running truly, same can be faced off to length—it should stand out 1/32 in. beyond the flanges—then centred, drilled No. 40 for 1/8 in. depth, and tapped 5 B.A. If a beginner overshoots in the drilling, and pierces the bore, he needn't fret about it, as the trunnion pin will prevent any leakage of steam. Reverse in chuck, and repeat operations; but before rechucking, ascertain if the two bosses are in line. If they aren't, which is very unlikely, make a centrepop on the unturned one, right opposite the tapped hole in the turned one, and chuck with the pop mark running truly.

If castings are supplied for the covers, turn and fit them in the same way as described for the covers of the engine cylinders. No gland is needed in the bottom cover. Just centre it, and put a No. 30 drill through. As the cylinder is single-acting, the space below the piston must be open to the atmosphere, so drill a No. 53 vent hole through the bottom cover. Castings are not really necessary for these weeny covers, I turn mine from brass rod. Chuck a piece of ¾ in. dia., face off, turn 1/32 in. to a push fit in the bore, and part off at 3/32 in. from the shoulder. Repeat operation for the bottom cover, but before parting

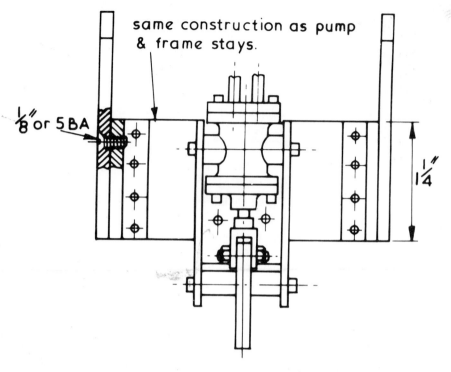

STEAM BRAKE CYLINDER ASSEMBLY

off, centre and drill No. 30 for about 5/16 in. depth, then part off at 7/32 in. from the shoulder. To turn the boss, rechuck in a little stepped bush made as described for the larger one used for holding the covers of the engine cylinders. Drill two No. 32 holes in the top cover for the pipe connecting the driver's brake valve, which will be fitted when we get to the cab details.

Making and fitting the piston and rod, is another job done in precisely the same way as those in the engine cylinders. Turn the piston from drawn rod; brass will do if nothing better is available. Rustless steel or bronze, 1/8 in. dia. will do for the piston-rod. The fork, or clevis as it is sometimes known, is made in exactly the same way as the valve-spindle crossheads on the big cylinders, so there is no need to go through the ritual again.

Stay and Bracket

The cross-stay and cylinder bracket can be combined in a single casting which requires little machining, and I prefer this type if available; but for those builders who prefer "fabricating", details of the built-up type are also shown. The cross-stay is made exactly as described for the pump and frame stays, and

may either have bent-over flanges, or flanges made from angle, riveted on.
. A piece of 13-gauge (3/32 in.) mild steel will be needed for the cylinder
bracket, 5 in. long and 2 in. wide. Mark off the outline of the bracket at one end
and at 13/16 in. from the back end, mark off a similar outline, but the other way
around. Cut away the surplus metal along the diagonal lines, and bend along
the vertical lines so that the result is channel-shape, as shown in the plan view.
Mark off the holes from the back end of the bracket after bending, so that both
sides line up. Attach the completed bracket to the stay by six 1/16 in. iron
rivets.

    If the combined casting is used, the sides should be machined off as described
for cast frame and pump stays, so that they fit nicely between the engine frames.
The insides of the projecting parts which carry the cylinder and brake shaft
should be smoothed off with a fine file. Take care that the holes on each side,
for the cylinder and shaft bearings, are exactly level. I usually mark off one side,
then centrepop the marks, set the casting on something level, like a surface
plate or the lathe bed, set the needle of a scribing-block to the centrepops, and
use it to mark off the other side. No bushes are needed, either in the built-up or
cast bracket. Pins through the plain drilled holes are quite satisfactory, as the
wear is infinitesimal.

    At 1¼ in. from the back end of the frame, on each side, drill three No. 30

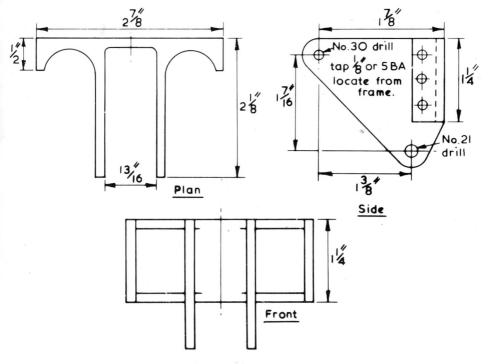

ALTERNATIVE COMBINED CAST BRACKET

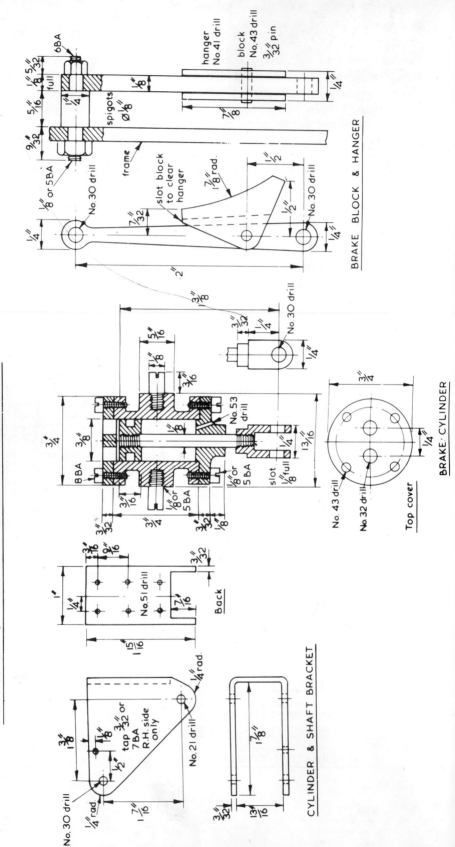

ARRANGEMENT OF VALVE GEAR FOR SLIDE VALVE CYLINDERS

BRAKE BLOCK & HANGER

BRAKE: CYLINDER

CYLINDER & SHAFT BRACKET

holes, the first at $\frac{1}{4}$ in. from the bottom, the others at 3/8 in. spacing, and countersink them. Smooth off any burring, then set the bracket in place with the bottom of the stay level with bottom of frame, and the back flush with the cut-away. Run the No. 30 drill through the holes in the frame, making countersinks on the bracket flanges; follow through with No. 40 drill, and tap 5 B.A., but don't put any screws in yet.

Brake Shaft

Chuck a piece of $\frac{1}{4}$ in. round mild steel, face the end, centre, drill No. 30 for about $\frac{1}{4}$ in. depth, and tap 5/32 in. × 40. Part off at a bare 13/16 in. from the end, reverse in chuck, and repeat drilling and tapping. Saw and file the bell-crank lever from 1/8 in. steel, an offcut from the frame will do, I save all my offcuts for jobs like this. Drill the hole for the brake shaft with letter C or 15/64

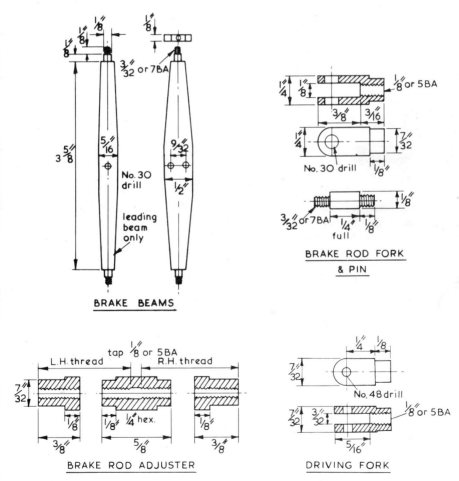

BRAKE BEAMS

BRAKE ROD FORK
& PIN

BRAKE ROD ADJUSTER

DRIVING FORK

drill, and ream it just enough to fit tightly on the shaft. Set it nicely in the middle, and braze it, as described previously for similar small jobs. Quench in water and clean up.

The pivots are made from 3/8 in. pieces of 5/32 in. silver-steel, one end screwed 5/32 in. × 40 for 3/16 in. length, and the other end slotted with a fine hacksaw, to take a screwdriver. To erect, just put the shaft in place between the sides of the bracket, and screw the pivots into it through the holes at each side.

The cylinder can also be erected. Pack the piston with a few strands of graphited yarn, put on the bottom cover (no gasket is needed) and screw on the fork tightly. Don't fit the top cover permanently, as it has to come off for attachment of pipes later on. Put the cylinder in place, with the fork over the end of the long arm of the brake lever, and secure it by screwing in the trunnion pins through the holes in the bracket. The trunnions are merely 5/16 in. lengths of 1/8 in. silver-steel, with 1/8 in. of thread to match the tapped holes in the bosses, at one end, and a screwdriver slot at the other. Pin the fork to the brake lever by a pin made from 1/8 in. silver-steel, turned down at each end, and screwed and nutted as shown for the forks on the brake rods. The bracket, with shaft and cylinder attached, can now be erected in the engine frame "for keeps", using 1/8 in. × 3/8 in. countersunk steel screws.

Pull-rods

The pull-rods are made from 1/8 in. round steel; either mild or silver-steel will do, or straight lengths of 1/8 in. iron wire would be quite satisfactory. Ten forks will be needed for connecting up; these are made from $\frac{1}{4}$ in. square mild steel, to the dimensions shown by the same process described for making the valve-spindle crosshead forks. Ten silver-steel pins are also required.

Put the forks in place on the brake beams, and put a pin temporarily in each. Next, with the chassis upside-down on the bench, measure carefully the distance between the forks, with the brake-blocks pressed against the wheel treads. Allow for about 5/32 in. entering the boss of each fork. Cut the rods to the measured lengths, and screw each end of them for about 3/16 in. length, to fit the bosses. Fit the forks to the first four pull-rods and adjust them so that when the pins are in, and nutted up, all the brake-blocks touch the wheel treads, at the same time, when the rear beam is pulled toward the back of the engine.

The fifth beam is connected to the short arm of the brake lever by a pull-rod with an adjuster on it. This requires a 5 B.A. left-hand tap and die; but anybody who hasn't these need not worry. Just fit a plain pull-rod, same as the others. Those who have, proceed as follows. Chuck a piece of $\frac{1}{4}$ in. hexagon rod in the three-jaw, face, centre, drill to $\frac{3}{4}$ in. depth with No. 40 drill, and tap to a full $\frac{1}{4}$ in. depth with 5 B.A. right-hand tap. Turn 1/8 in. length to 7/32 in. dia. and part off at 5/8 in. from the end. Reverse in chuck, turn down the other end likewise, and tap the remains of the hole with a 5 B.A. left-hand tap. Mark on the outside which is which!

Chuck the hexagon rod again, centre, drill No. 40 to ½ in. depth, tap 5 B.A. right-hand thread, turn ¼ in. length to 7/32 in. dia. and part off at 3/8 in. from the end. Ditto repeat, but this time use a left-hand tap. That completes the adjuster. Cut a 1 in. length of 1/8 in. rod, screw one end 5 B.A. for 1/8 in. length, and the other for 5/8 in. length. Screw the short end into a fork, and pin it to the short arm of the brake lever. Put on the long adjuster nut tapped R.H. and screw on the R.H. end of the middle section of the adjuster.

Finally, hold the adjuster horizontally, and measure from it to the fork on the rear brake beam. Cut a piece of 1/8 in. rod to 5/16 in. longer than this measurement. Screw one end for 1/8 in. length, right-hand thread, and the other end 5/8 in. length, left-hand thread. Put the left-hand adjuster nut on this end, and screw the rod into the L.H. end of the middle part of the adjuster. Remove the fork from the brake beam, screw it on to the pull rod, and replace, putting in the pin. Adjustment is made by running the long adjusting nuts right back as far as they will go, and turning the centre part to right or left as required. With the piston at the top of its stroke, the brake-blocks should be quite clear of the wheel treads. When the correct adjustment is obtained, run the long adjuster nuts up to the centre section and tighten them, but not enough to risk stripping the threads.

When the driver's brake valve is operated, steam is admitted to the cylinder, forces down the piston, and the long arm of the brake lever, and "plonks 'em on" as the drivers say. When steam is released from the cylinder by shifting the driver's valve to the "off" position, a spring pulls up the brake lever, and releases the blocks from contact with the wheel treads. The spring is wound up from 19-gauge tinned steel wire. One end is attached to the brake arm by a 7 B.A. screw, and the other end to the cylinder bracket near the top in similar fashion.

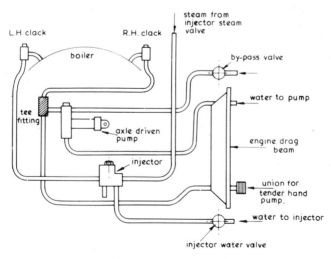

DIAGRAM OF PIPE CONNECTIONS

The chassis and smokebox   (photograph by K Pietron)

Evening Star under construction r.h. side   (photograph by K Pietron)

The boiler fitted to the smokebox and frames   (photograph by K Pictron)

K Pietron seen driving his "Evening Star" on a ground level track   (photograph by K Pietron)

CHAPTER ELEVEN

First Details of the Boiler

There are a few more oddments needed to complete the chassis, such as cylinder cocks and so on, but if builders are anything like me, they will be glad to give the fiddling jobs a rest, and get on with the boiler. For beginners' benefit I might explain that while a small locomotive boiler can be made to resemble that of the full-size article very closely, as far as external appearance goes, the inside of it has to conform to the laws of Nature, if the boiler is to be a successful steamer. The boiler is similar to that which I specified for *Britannia* and several other 4-6-2 locomotives, and although it looks rather complicated at first sight, there is nothing very difficult about the actual building, as many beginners have agreeably discovered.

It isn't the actual size of a boiler, nor the maximum number of square inches of heating surface, that ensures successful steaming. It is the way the heating surface is arranged, and most important of all, the amount of heat applied to that surface. The domestic kettle boils up quickly enough if it is placed on a gas ring, but not so quickly if you put a candle underneath it, though the size of the kettle and the heating surface of the bottom of it remain unchanged! The most valuable part of the heating surface of a locomotive boiler is the firebox, the plates of which get direct heat both by radiation and convection. Long tubes are not efficient, because there is a considerable difference between the temperature of the firebox gases in the tubes, at the ends nearest the firebox, and the smoke-box ends. Now in a long-barrelled boiler such as *Evening Star's*, we can kill two birds with one shot, and obtain maximum efficiency, if we increase the heating surface of the firebox by adding a combustion chamber; and as this automatically shortens the tubes—well, as they say in the classics, Bob's your uncle!

The idea is, of course, not new; there is nothing new under the sun. McConnell, Beattie, Cudworth and others used combustion-chambers in full-size boiler barrels way back in the Victorian era, but for different purposes. Old ideas can, however, be mighty useful if brought up to date. In my experimenting, I found that by making the combined length of firebox and combustion chamber approximately equal to the length of the tubes, and staying the combustion chamber by means of stout water-tube struts, best part of the heat from the fire was transferred to the water, the smokebox remaining com-

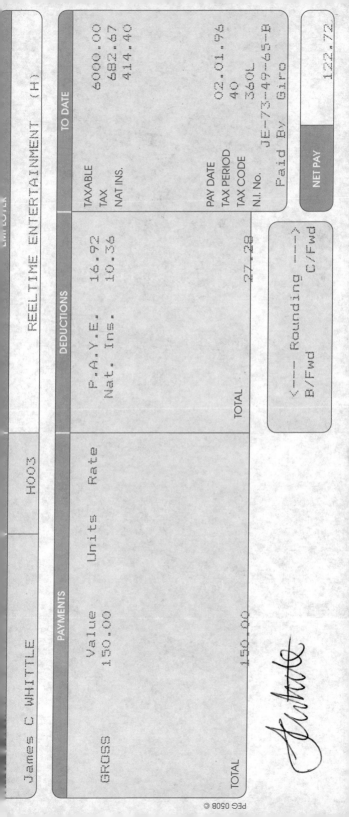

James C WHITTLE   H003   REELTIME ENTERTAINMENT (H)

PAYMENTS

	Value	Units	Rate
GROSS	150.00		
TOTAL	150.00		

DEDUCTIONS

P.A.Y.E.	16.92
Nat. Ins.	10.36
TOTAL	27.28

TO DATE

TAXABLE	6000.00
TAX	682.67
NAT INS.	414.40

PAY DATE	02.01.96
TAX PERIOD	40
TAX CODE	360L
N.I. No.	JE-73-49-65-B
	Paid By Giro

<--- Rounding --->
B/Fwd   C/Fwd

NET PAY   122.72

© PEG 0508

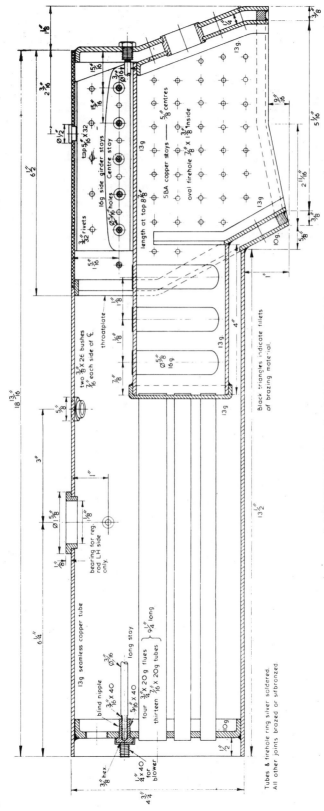

LONGITUDINAL SECTION OF BOILER

Tubes & firehole ring silver soldered.
All other joints brazed or siftbronzed.

Black triangles indicate fillets of brazing material.

paratively cool. None of my own engines ever suffered from blistered paint on the smokebox, and that was good proof.

Tube diameter was another important factor. If too small, they become choked. If too large they don't pick up the heat as they should but allow a kind of core of heated gas to pass through the middle and be blown to waste up the chimney. Superheater flues must of necessity be large, but as the elements carrying the steam are in the middle, the hot core is utilised to heat them. In the boiler shown, there will be one complete element in each flue. Some of my own locomotives have 1 in. flues with two elements in each, and I prefer this, but had I specified them for *Evening Star* there wouldn't have been sufficient space for the requisite number of smaller tubes. Hence the arrangement shown. I have also done quite a lot of experimenting to find the simplest method of construction, yet at the same time able to stand all the stresses to which the boiler might be subjected.

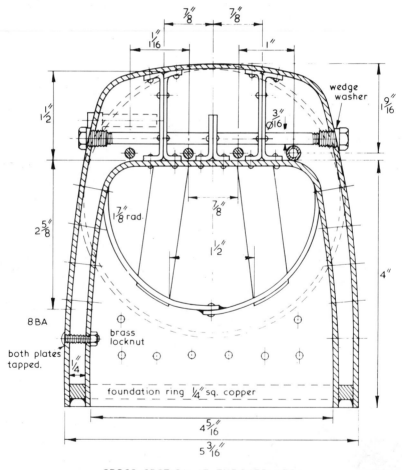

CROSS SECTION AT THROATPLATE:

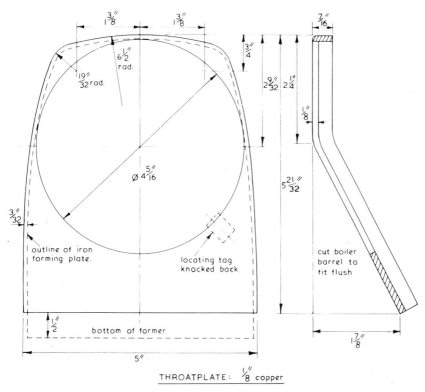

THROATPLATE: $\frac{1}{8}''$ copper

The final results are embodied in the boiler shown. So much for that; now to the actual job of building the boiler, with some tips for beginners.

Tools for the Job

For a brazing pan, a rectangular iron tray not less than 2 ft. long, 1 ft. wide, about 2 in. deep at front and 8 in. or more at the back, will be required. My own is made from 16-gauge sheet steel. A hefty pair of blacksmiths' tongs will be needed for holding the boiler when hot, and a small pair for holding short lengths of brazing material. I made mine from 1/8 in. × 5/16 in. black mild steel strip, with handles a foot long. To break up flux bubbles, bend one end of an 18 in. length of 1/8 in. iron wire into a ring, and file the other end to a point. If an oxy-acetylene blowpipe isn't available, a propane blowpipe of about 1.½ in. dia. will be required, or its equivalent in air-gas blowpipes; also a smaller one for the lighter jobs.

The brazing material can be any good brand silver-solder with the special flux sold for use with it. For tubes and bushes, use either best grade silversolder in strip form, with powdered borax as flux, or "Easyflo" and the special flux sold with it.

A leaden or earthenware container big enough to hold the boiler will be needed for pickling or cleaning the boiler after each stage of the brazing operations. Special advice to beginners—never work on a dirty boiler. You'll not only get unsound joints, but probably skin troubles as well should any of the stuff on dirty copper find its way into stray cuts or scratches. I made my pickle bath, which is approximately 2 ft. × 1 ft. from a sheet of lead 1/16 in. thick, bending it up like a painter makes a paper box for holding small quantities of paint. It is seamless, and therefore leak proof. When new, I put it in a wooden box to prevent it getting knocked about; but the wood has long since rotted away, leaving the lead "naked and unashamed". I keep a lid on it, to prevent rainwater getting in and diluting the solution too much, or causing overflow. The pickle is the same as I have mentioned for small jobs, viz. one part commercial sulphuric acid to about 16 of water, or one part stale accumulator acid to four of water.

Most important tip of all—if you can possibly do your brazing in the open air, that's the best place. If inside, make sure that there is adequate ventilation. I keep my oxy-acet cylinders alongside the forge, and also laid in a coal-gas pipe, so everything is nice and handy and no time is wasted. Now to business.

Boiler Barrel

The boiler barrel is made from a piece of 3/32 in. (13-gauge) seamless copper tube 4.$\frac{3}{4}$ in. outside dia. and a full 13.$\frac{1}{2}$ in. long. One end must be trued up in the lathe. Plug each end with a disc of wood. Grip one end truly in the four-jaw chuck, and run the tailstock centre into the middle of the other end to a depth of

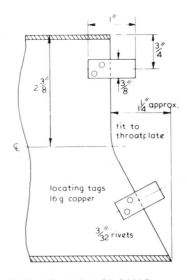

BACK END OF BOILER BARREL

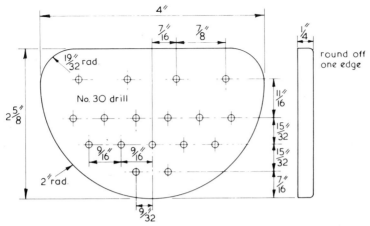

FORMER & TUBE DRILLING JIG FOR COMBUSTION
CHAMBER TUBEPLATE

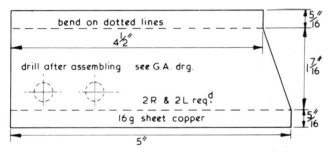

SIDE CROWNSTAY PLATES BEFORE BENDING

about 3/16 in. enough to prevent it from slipping under cut. Run the lathe at
slow speed, and trim up the edge of the tube truly, with a roundnose tool set in
the rest at an angle. Apply some cutting oil to the job with a brush, or the
copper will probably tear. Keep the tool sharp, as copper is finicky stuff to turn,
and slightly round off the edges of the tube, to avoid risk of cut fingers.

The other end of the tube has to be shaped to fit the throatplate. At 1.¼ in.
from the end, scribe a line on the tube projecting down 2.1/8 in. from the top. I
use a flexible steel rule for this job, keeping it flat on the copper and at right
angles to the tube. Grip the tube in the bench vice (leave the wood plug in, to
avoid distortion) and with a 32-tooth blade in the hacksaw frame, carefully saw
down to the end of the line. A brushful of cutting oil on the saw blade helps a
wonderful lot. Now turn the tube the other way up, and saw down diagonally to
meet the first cut. If the vice jaws won't open wide enough to take the tube, an
extra inch or so can often be managed by removing the two steel insets from the
jaw tops. Trimming up the saw-cuts and fitting the locating tags, must be left
until the throatplate and outer firebox assembly is made.

Throatplate

The throatplate is made from 1/8 in. (10-gauge) sheet copper, and is flanged over an iron forming-plate, or former, as it is called. Formers can be sawn from $\frac{1}{4}$ in. iron or steel plate. Hard wood has been used, but where more than one plate has to be flanged, wooden formers aren't very satisfactory, as they won't stand up to the terrific bashing that has no effect on metal ones. To make one, mark out on a piece of iron or soft steel plate, the outline shown dotted on the drawing of the throatplate making it $\frac{1}{2}$ in. longer at the bottom, to allow for the bend in the throatplate. Saw to outline, using a coarse-toothed blade, say 14 teeth per inch, and plenty of cutting oil. Tip for beginners: take slow steady strokes, pressing down heavily on the forward stroke, and you'll be surprised by the way the saw walks through the metal. Trim the sawn edges with a file, and round off one edge of the curved part.

Lay the former on a piece of 1/8 in. sheet copper, and mark a line all around, except at bottom, a full 5/16 in. away from the former, but keeping to the exact shape. I cut out my copper plates with a Driver jig-saw, using a 32-tooth blade

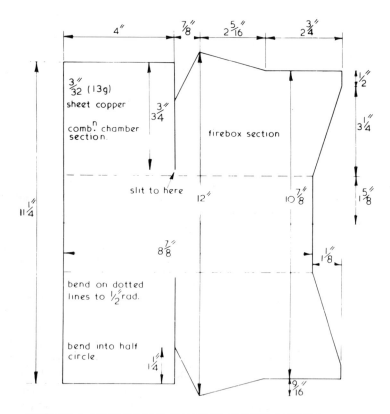

FIREBOX & COMBUSTION CHAMBER BEFORE BENDING

lubricated with beeswax; but an ordinary piercing-saw (glorified hand fretsaw) can be used, lubricated with cutting oil. No need to file out the sawmarks. Heat the copper to medium red, in the domestic fire or over a gas ring, then drop it into a pail of clean cold water. Place the former in the middle of it, rounded edge next to the copper, and grip the lot in the bench vice tightly, with one edge projecting about $\frac{1}{2}$ in. above the jaws. Then, with a 2-lb. hammer, beat down the edge of the copper over the former. Repeat operation until the whole of the curved edge has been flanged.

Beware of cracking. Copper goes hard when hammered; so re-anneal it by heating and quenching as mentioned above, two or three times if necessary, during the flanging process. Smooth off the ragged edges and clean up the flanges all around, with a coarse file. The scratches form a champion "key" for the brazing material.

At 2.9/32 in. from the top, and midway between sides, make a centrepop, and from this, scribe a circle 4.5/16 in. dia. Cut around this with a piercing-saw, or drill a circle of 1/8 in. holes, breaking out the piece and trimming to size with a half-round file. At 2.¼ in. from the top, saw a V-shaped piece out of the flange at each side. This will allow the lower part of the throatplate to be bent back easily until the bottom edge is 1.7/8 in. behind the upper part. This will raise the lower part of the hole, so file away the copper until the hole is 4.5/16 in. from top to bottom measured vertically.

Firebox Wrapper

The best way to get the shape and size of the piece of sheet copper required for the firebox wrapper plate, is to use a paper pattern, or template. In my childhood days, a dressmaker to whom I rendered some services, taught me a lot about paper patterns, but never dreamed of the use to which I would put her teaching! Cut a piece of thick brown paper about 15 in. × 8 in. and lay it around the flange of the throatplate. Keep it in close contact with a clip at the bottom of each side.

The front edge of the paper should be flush with the upper part of the throatplate. Snip off the lower part to the same angle as the throatplate. On the lower and back edges of the paper, mark with a pencil the outlines of the bottom edges of the firebox and the edge of the firebox backhead, and cut away the surplus paper. The result should be a paper replica of the firebox wrapper sheet.

Remove it from the throatplate, flatten it out, lay it on a piece of 3/32 in. (13-gauge) sheet copper, and scribe around it, to mark the outline on the copper. Alternatively, stick the paper pattern on the copper, same as a kiddy would do with a fretsaw pattern; then saw and file to outline. If the copper is hard, soften it as described previously, then bend it to shape so that it fits closely to the throatplate flange. Mark off the location of the corner bends, then put a piece of round steel rod in the vice jaws. This should be about 9/16 in. dia. and

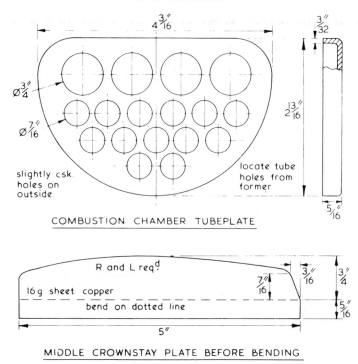

COMBUSTION CHAMBER TUBEPLATE

MIDDLE CROWNSTAY PLATE BEFORE BENDING

project about 7 in. from the side of the vice. Lay the copper over the rod at the place where the bend is to be, and give each side a good hearty downward press simultaneously. Beginners will be surprised how easily the bend is made. Ditto repeat at the other top corner, then try the wrapper over the throatplate flange. Naturally it won't fit exactly at first go, but it won't want much coaxing to get it fitting nicely over the flange. Clean around the inside, where the wrapper is in contact with the flange, with coarse emery cloth or similar abrasive; then rivet the wrapper to the flange with 3/32 in. copper rivets. Only a few are needed, say about 1.½ in. apart. They have nothing to do with the strength of the boiler, being merely for the purpose of keeping the parts together while the brazing job is under way. No need for fancy snapped heads as they are filed flush after brazing.

Assembly

The next item is to fit the barrel to the throatplate. Try it in place, and if it doesn't line up truly, with the shaped end of the barrel in close contact with the throatplate, teach it good manners with a file. The top of the barrel and top of the wrapper should form a straight line and the sides should be parallel also. I never bother about any fixture between barrel and throatplate; all I do is to stand the completed firebox shell in the brazing pan, with the barrel perched on top of it in correct position, and get busy with my oxyacet blowpipe; but I don't recommend that lark for beginners and inexperienced coppersmiths.

To hold the assembly securely in place, rivet four locating tags to the inside of the barrel. They are 1 in. lengths of 16-gauge copper about $\frac{3}{4}$ in. wide, and should project about $\frac{1}{2}$ in. from the barrel. Push them through the big hole in the throatplate when fitting the barrel for keeps, and when it is correctly located, knock back the ends of the tags against the inside of the throatplate. That will prevent the barrel shifting while brazing the joint.

First Brazing Job

Put a layer of small coke or blacksmith's breeze in the bottom of the pan, and stand the assembly on it with the barrel pointing to the sky. Pile up the coke at sides and back almost to the level of the throatplate, and inside the wrapper to about 1 in. below it. Mix up some flux to a creamy paste with water, and well cover the joints with it, especially the top corners where barrel, wrapper and throatplate form a sort of triangle, and at the side joints between wrapper and throatplate, below the barrel. Have everything handy close to the pan, which should stand on an iron frame, or a few bricks at each side would do. If using a blowlamp, see that there is plenty of paraffin in it, as the job will be spoiled if it goes out when the boiler is hot, and get it going good and strong to start with. Tip for beginners: the secret of good brazing is ample heat in the right place, plus clean metal.

Heat the assembly evenly by moving the flame about over the copper, then play on the coke around and inside it. When the coke glows red, concentrate the flame on one bottom corner of the throatplate. When that reaches bright red dip the piece of brazing strip into the flux, then apply it to the joint in the flame. If the heat is right, the end of the strip will melt and flow into the joint. Now move the flame along very slowly, an inch or so at a time, and as the copper glows bright red, apply more brazing strip, dipping it in the flux at each application. When the barrel is reached, keep right on, playing the flame on barrel, wrapper and throatplate, and feeding in the brazing material as the metal becomes red under the flame. When you get to the top, where the barrel separates from the joint between throatplate and wrapper, direct the flame so that the lot is heated simultaneously. Feed in plenty of brazing material, and fill up the whole corner to a flush surface, the molten spelter forming a fillet against the barrel.

Carry on over the top, give the other corner a dose of the same medicine, then work your way downwards. When the lower part of the barrel is reached where it leaves the side of the wrapper to form the "belly" part, play the flame direct on the joint between barrel and throatplate, and feed in sufficient brazing material to form a fillet. When the end of the joint is finally reached, at the point where the barrel meets the wrapper again, give an extra blow-up, and feed in more spelter to ensure that the joint is continuous and perfectly sound. If, during the operation, there is any bubbling of the molten spelter, scratch it with the pointed wire, in the flame, otherwise what are known as borax bubbles or blisters will form, and leakage will develop. Then finish off the side joints.

Finally, let the job cool, then carefully put it in the pickle bath—and mind the splashes! Let it soak 15 minutes or so, then fish it out, well wash in running water, and clean it up with a handful of steel wool, or some domestic scouring powder.

Firebox and Combustion Chamber

The top and sides of the firebox and the barrel of the combustion chamber are made from a single sheet of 13-gauge copper, measuring 12 in. × 10 in. To assist beginners and inexperienced coppersmiths the drawings show this "in the flat". The first job is to mark out very carefully the outline shown to the given dimensions on a piece of thick brown paper or drawing paper. Cut it exactly to the outline and don't forget the deep slits at either side at 4 in. from the straight edge. Bend up the paper template and fix the overlap at the bottom of the barrel section with a pin or a couple of paper clips. Now check off your paper dummy with the longitudinal and cross-sections of the firebox and combustion chamber shown in the general arrangement of the whole boiler. If O.K. go ahead and mark out the sheet of copper, using the paper template as a guide. Cut the copper to outline, soften it, bend to shape and fix the lap joint with four

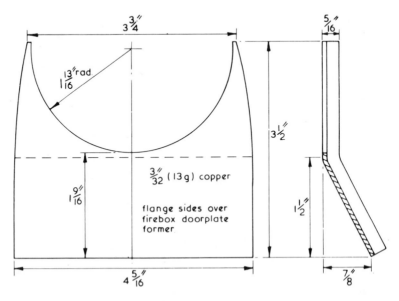

FIREBOX   THROATPLATE

copper rivets to keep it close set while the brazing is under way.

Experienced coppersmiths can, of course, mark out direct on the 12 in. × 10 in. sheet of copper, and bend up right away, but for tyros and first-timers it is far better—and cheaper!—to make the paper dummy first. If you spoil 20 pieces of paper all you lose is your time, but if you make an apple pie of just one sheet of copper, well—copper sheet is mighty expensive nowadays!

Firebox Throatplate

The front end of the firebox section is closed by a throatplate somewhat similar to the larger one previously described, but it has to extend only to the upper part of the barrel of the combustion chamber. As the throatplate and firebox doorplate are flanged over the same forming plate make this first. Use $\frac{1}{4}$ in. iron or steel plate, cut to the shape of the firebox doorplate but 1/16 in. less in width at each side and $\frac{1}{2}$ in. longer at bottom. File off the upper edge to the angle shown. One edge of sides and top should be rounded off.

A piece of 13-gauge sheet copper 4 in. × 5 in. will be needed for the throatplate. Lay the former on it and scribe a line 5/16 in. away from each side, then cut away the superfluous metal. Set your dividers to 1.13/16 in. radius and on the centre line at $3\frac{1}{2}$ in. from the bottom strike the arc shown. Saw out the semi-circular segment, then grip former and plate together in the bench vice and flange the sides. Nick the flange at each side at $1\frac{1}{2}$ in. from the bottom and bend the lower part backwards. Clean the flanges with a coarse file and well

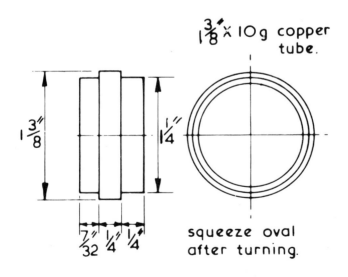

$1\frac{3}{8}$" × 10g copper tube.

squeeze oval after turning.

FIREHOLE RING

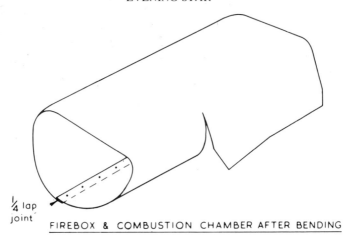

$\frac{1}{4}$ lap
joint
FIREBOX & COMBUSTION CHAMBER AFTER BENDING

clean the copper below the cut-away part to ensure sound brazed joints. Finally put the throatplate in position at the front of the firebox and rivet the flanges to the front end of the side sheets with five 3/32 in. copper rivets at each side.

Beginners especially note that flanges must be in the closest possible contact with the sides of the firebox and the front must butt up as tightly as possible against the edge of the combustion chamber. In full-size practice the joint is flanged and riveted, but the big boilers are not brazed and a flanged joint is needed to stand up to the stress. In the small boiler the brazing material forms a fillet, which replaces the flange and, if properly done, is actually stronger than the metal of the boiler itself. I've built a good many boilers with firebox throatplates made as above and have never had even a leak, let alone a failure. Experiences teaches!

Firebox Doorplate

The firebox doorplate will need a piece of 13-gauge sheet copper 4.1/8 in. × 5.1/16 in. Lay the forming plate on this with the upper edge 3/8 in. below the edge of the copper and scribe a line at each side 5/16 in. away from the former. Cut to outline, soften the copper, then grip copper and former together in the bench vice and flange the sides and top in the manner previously described, taking care to get the round corners at the top nicely bedded down to the edge of the former. At $\frac{1}{2}$ in. from the bottom, at each side, nick the flanges and bend the plate as shown.

Clean the flange all round with a coarse file so that the brazed joint will be sound. At $1\frac{1}{2}$ in. from the top, on the centre line, mark out the oval shown for the firehole ring, but don't cut the hole until the ring is made.

The type of firehole ring shown (see general arrangement drawing for a section of it) was originally designed by a Brighton works friend now deceased

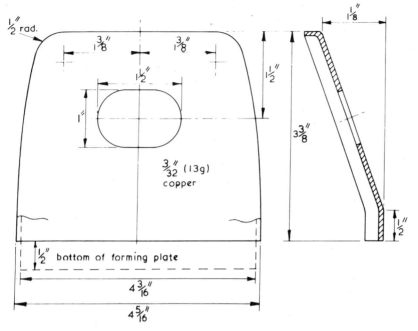

$\frac{1}{2}$" rad.

$1\frac{3}{8}$" $1\frac{3}{8}$"

$1\frac{1}{2}$"

$\frac{1}{2}$"

$1\frac{1}{2}$"

1"

$3\frac{3}{8}$"

$\frac{3}{32}$" (13g)
copper

$\frac{1}{8}$"

$\frac{1}{2}$"

$\frac{1}{2}$" bottom of forming plate

$4\frac{3}{16}$"

$4\frac{5}{16}$"

FIREBOX DOORPLATE

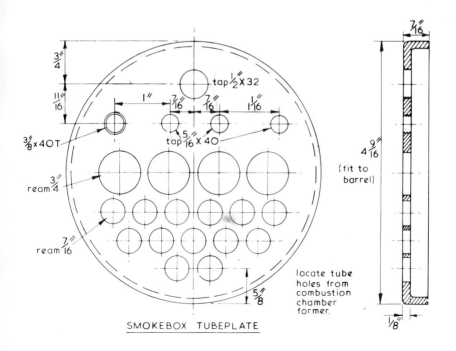

$\frac{3}{4}$"

$\frac{11}{16}$"

tap $\frac{1}{2}$ X 32

1" $\frac{7}{16}$" $\frac{7}{16}$" $1\frac{1}{16}$"

$\frac{3}{8}$ X 40 T

tap $\frac{5}{16}$ X 40

ream $\frac{3}{4}$"

ream $\frac{7}{16}$"

$\frac{5}{8}$"

locate tube
holes from
combustion
chamber
former.

$\frac{7}{16}$"

$4\frac{9}{16}$"

(fit to
barrel)

$\frac{1}{8}$"

SMOKEBOX TUBEPLATE

and is the best type of ring for small boilers that I ever tried. It needs no riveting, no plate flanging, and forms a substantial stay between the firebox doorplate and backhead. It is made from a piece of copper tube 1.3/8 in. diameter and 1/8 in. thick. Chuck in three jaw, face the end and turn down $\frac{1}{4}$ in. length to 1.$\frac{1}{4}$ in. diameter. Part off at a bare $\frac{3}{4}$ in. from the end, reverse in chuck and turn down a full 7/32 in. length to 1.$\frac{1}{4}$ in. diameter, leaving $\frac{1}{4}$ in. full diameter between the shoulders. Anneal by heating to medium red and plunging into clean cold water, then squeeze the ring into an oval shape in the bench vice until the hole measures 1.3/8 in. $\times$ 7/8 in. The exact radius of the ends doesn't matter.

Lay the oval ring on the firebox doorplate at the marked place and scribe a line around it. Cut out the piece, then push the 7/32 in. end of the ring through, from the outside of the doorplate, and beat the projecting lip of the flange outward and downward until the metal of the doorplate is firmly gripped between the shoulder of the ring and the beaten-down flange. The rear end of the firebox can then be cleaned on the inner side with coarse emery cloth or similar abrasive (the more scratches made in the copper the better the joint after brazing) the doorplate inserted so that it is flush with the ends and a few 3/32 in. copper rivets put through flange and plate to keep the parts in position for brazing.

Combustion Chamber Tubeplate

The end of the combusion chamber is closed by a flanged plate which fits over the end like the lid of a coffee tin. The former, over which this is flanged, must therefore be the same size as the end of the chamber. It also serves as a jig to drill the tube holes in both the combustion chamber and smokebox tubeplates, as both should be alike. Either use the iron casting supplied by our advertisers or saw the former from $\frac{1}{4}$ in. steel plate as before, rounding off one edge. Set out very carefully the location of the tube holes. The horizontal spacing of the tube holes, the lower rows, is 9/16 in. and the vertical spacing is 15/32 in. The centres of the holes for the superheater flues are 11/16 in. above the upper row of small tubes and the horizontal spacing is 7/8 in. Make deep centrepops so that the drill won't wander when starting to penetrate, then drill the lot No. 30.

The piece of 13-gauge copper required will be 4.5/8 in. $\times$ 3.$\frac{1}{4}$ in. Lay the drilled former on it, scribe a line all round 5/16 in. away from the former, cut away the surplus, soften the copper and flange it over the former as before. This time, before removing the flanged copper plate from the former, run the No. 30 drill through all the holes, carrying on right through the copper. Clean the flange with a 27/64 in. drill. Tip for beginners: if you haven't a machine vice big enough to hold the tubeplate while drilling don't attempt to hold it with your fingers. Soft copper is finicky stuff to drill and the chances are a million dollars to a pinch of snuff that the drill will catch up just as it breaks through, the tube-plate will spin and in a split second your fingers will be in a bluepencil mess where the sharp edge of the copper has caught them. The way to avoid this is to put a piece of hard wood on the drilling machine table, lay the tubeplate on it flange upward, and either grip the flange with a "Foot-print" wrench or something similar, or else grip it with a thick piece of cloth or rag. Press the plate down to the wood as tightly as possible, run the drill at slow speed and apply plenty of cutting oil. The hardwood backing will prevent the drill from catching up and the cutting oil will ease it through.

Open up the top row of holes with a 47/64 in. drill and true them up with a $\frac{3}{4}$ in. parallel reamer. Don't put it right through, only insert the "lead" end far enough to bring the hole to a true circle. Ditto repeat the smaller holes using a 7/16 in. parallel reamer. Slightly countersink the lot on the side opposite to the flange, then clean the inside of the flange and the end of the combustion chamber and "put the lid on". It should fit very tightly.

Crown Stays

Rod stays are used in full-size practice between firebox crown sheet and the outside shell, but as Nature refuses to be "scaled" this type isn't suitable for a boiler of the size we are building. Erosion takes place at the same speed whatever the size of the boiler and, while a loss of, say, 1/16 in. would make

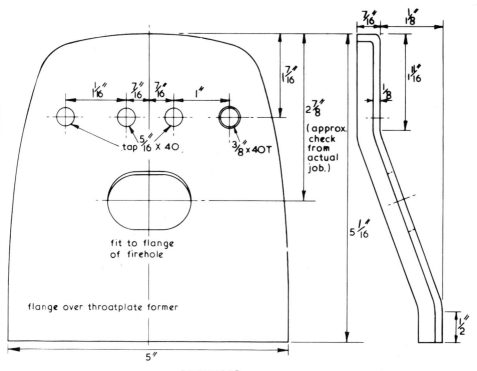

BACKHEAD

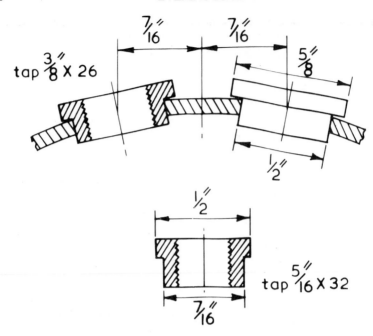

SAFETY VALVE & TURRET BUSHES

little appreciable difference to a full-size rod stay, it would weaken a little one to breaking point in a short time. I once saw the crown sheet of a rod-stayed firebox collapse at a local club exhibition and afterwards held a post-mortem on the remains. The rod stays, $1\frac{1}{2}$ in. long and 1/8 in. diameter, had wasted away to the thickness of a domestic pin at the middle. They were made of the alloy used for making commercial brass screws.

Girder stays are the best to use for small locomotive boilers for supporting the crown sheet. They are easy to make and fit, there is freedom from leakage, and they convert the back end of the boiler into what is virtually a box girder, one of the strongest forms of construction. My pet version is shown in the longitudinal and cross-sections of the boiler. The side stays are each made up of two-channel sections riveted back to back and the middle one is formed by two angles. To make the side stays cut four pieces of 16-gauge sheet copper to the dimensions shown, bend the flanges in the bench vice and rivet each pair back to back with nine 3/32 in. copper rivets. The middle stay is formed from two pieces of 1/16 in. sheet copper, cut and bent as shown and riveted together with the flanges outwards.

As the cross-stays supporting the upper part of the firebox wrapper have to pass through the girders, drill five 5/16 in. holes in each in the position shown in the longitudinal section of the boiler, then rivet the middle one to the top of the firebox, on the centre line, and the other two with their vertical centre lines at

7/8 in. on either side of it, bringing the distance between the inner sides of the plates to 1.5/8 in. Use 3/32 in. copper rivets at approximately 1.¼ in. centres with the heads inside the firebox. Make sure that the crown stay flanges bed tightly down to the firebox top for their full length.

Water-tube struts

The flat top of the combustion chamber is stayed by the six slightly-inclined water-tubes, which not only add to the heating surface in a really hot place but keep the water in lively circulation. Scribe a line along the middle of the top of the chamber and a parallel line at each side ¾ in. away. On each of the latter make a centrepop 7/8 in. from the end of the chamber and two more at 1.1/8 in. intervals. On the underside scribe two parallel lines at 1.1/8 in. each side of the lap joint and centrepop them likewise. Drill the whole bunch first with a 3/16 in. drill, then open them out with a 39/64 in. drill, then bring them to size with a 5/8 in. parallel reamer. Ream each hole singly at first to true it up as drills usually make polysided holes in sheet metal, then put the reamer through each pair of holes at once, which will line them up to receive the tubes. Countersink all the holes slightly, which will help the brazing material to flow easily all around the ends of the tubes. To countersink holes on a curved surface use a small half-round file.

The water-tubes are seamless copper, 5/8 in. diameter × 16 gauge. Saw off six 2.¾ in. lengths and drive them through the holes in the combustion chamber as shown in the cross-section of the firebox. Leave the ends as sawn for the time being; just see that they project an equal amount from the top and bottom of the chamber. They should fit tightly and the ends should be well cleaned.

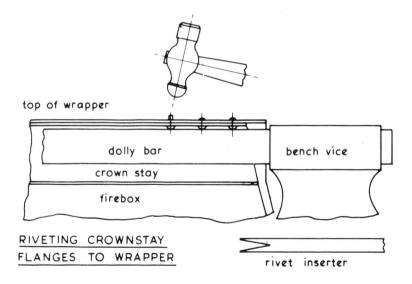

top of wrapper

dolly bar   bench vice

crown stay

firebox

RIVETING CROWNSTAY
FLANGES TO WRAPPER

rivet inserter

Brazing the Assembly

First well cover all the joints and seams with wet flux, putting a good dose all along the crown-stay flanges where they are attached to the top of the firebox and plenty around the firehole ring. Fill up the interstices where the throat and door plates are riveted to the firebox sides. Now stand the assembly on end in the brazing pan with the combustion chamber tubeplate resting on the coke. There should be a good fillet of wet flux all around the flange. First play the blowpipe flame over the whole assembly to get it well warmed up and also to dry the moisture out of the flux, which should then stick to all the joints. If it doesn't they will oxidise and the brazing material won't "take".

Next concentrate the flame on the tubeplate flange and the end of the combustion chamber. The part which the flame licks should become bright red in a matter of seconds as the red-hot coke will help matters. Dip the end of the silver-solder in the flux, apply it to the flange in the flame and, if the heat is O.K., the strip will melt off and the molten metal will flow into the joint between flange and chamber. Work your way slowly and carefully right around the flange, feeding in the brazing strip as the metal becomes red, and don't forget to keep dipping the end of the strip into the flux. Beginners have nothing to fear; as soon as the first bit of brazing material has melted and flowed into the joint the "technique" comes naturally to anybody of average intelligence and they find themselves manipulating the flame and feeding in the strip as though they had served an apprenticeship with a professional coppersmith. On completing the circuit and arriving back at the starting point give an extra blow so that the molten metal flows easily and makes the joint continuous. There should be a nice even fillet all around the joint.

To avoid shifting the hot firebox more than necessary the doorplate can next be tackled. As the whole box of tricks is now well heated, just play the flame on the near-side bottom corner. As soon as it glows bright red apply the brazing strip, and when it melts and flows, work your way right around, slowly and carefully, to the off-side bottom corner. Halfway around you'll meet the firehole ring. Concentrate the flame on it and when it and the surrounding copper glows bright red apply the strips and a fillet of molten metal should flow right around it. Alternatively, a strip of coarse-grade silver solder could be used on the ring joint, as this runs like water at a dull red heat and penetrates more deeply into the joint than regular spelter.

Next by aid of the big tongs, turn the assembly the other way up, letting the doorplate rest on the coke. Then get to work on the throatplate, starting at the near-side bottom corner, working up to the combustion chamber, going along the "belly" joint and then down the other side. Two warnings here: Make sure that the molten brazing material flows into and seals each end of the cut between firebox and combustion chamber. Secondly, feed enough strip into the "belly" joint to ensure a fillet not less than 1/8 in, deep right from one end to the other. The firebox will then have an ample margin of strength and will never sprout Welsh vegetables.

Turn the assembly the right way up and lay a strip of silver solder along each of the crownstay flanges. As mentioned above, this material melts more easily and penetrates better than regular spelter and so I recommend it for this particular job. Play the blowlamp flame on the flanges and the firebox top until the bits of silver solder melt and flow in between the flanges and the crown sheet. This will also seal the rivets. Now go along to the projecting bits of water-tube. Play on each separately until it and the surrounding copper becomes bright red, then run a fillet of spelter around each, which should completely fill the countersink and project a little above it. Finally, turn the assembly upside down and give the other ends of the water-tubes a dose of the same medicine, sealing the lap joint at the same heating.

Let the lot cool to black, take a look at the joints and seams and make sure that nothing has been missed, then put the assembly in the pickle for about 20 minutes. Wash it well in running water and clean it up with steel wool or scouring powder. Saw off the projecting ends of the water-tubes and finish with a file until they stand about 1/32 in. proud of the combustion-chamber.

The technique is different with an oxycoal-gas blowpipe as the flame of this is much hotter, only a small nozzle of about $\frac{1}{4}$ in. dia. is needed. The patch of redhot copper under the flame will be smaller, but hotter, and care must be taken to avoid overheating. If smoke and a greenish flame comes up from the molten spelter, go easy, or else you'll have had it. Burnt copper is unsafe for boiler work. In technical books dealing with brazing and bronze-welding, a nozzle of about 5/32 in. dia. is specified for oxy-coal-gas blowpipes on copper work similar to the *Evening Star* boiler, but as this needs a fairly high oxygen pressure, the risk of a beginner burning the copper is greater than if a larger nozzle with lower oxygen pressure is needed. This gives a more diffused flame, and if the flame is "lined up" with the job the risk of burning is small.

CHAPTER TWELVE

Oxy-acetylene boilersmithing

In January 1932 I purchased a No. 2 "Alda" oxy-acetylene outfit, and as a famous soap advertisement used to say, "since then I have used no other" for all my boiler work. While a large propane blowpipe does the job all right, there is no denying that the sight and sound of it in full blast is rather awesome; and the contrast between it and the small bluish flame with the white cone at the root, plus the sibilant hiss, is most marked. The great advantage is that the most heat can be put exactly where you want it, and as there is little heat radiated back on the operator, the job can be done in comfort. In my blowlamp days, the buttons on my overall often became too hot to touch when doing the final brazing job on a boiler, and on one occasion a fountain-pen inadvertently left in the top pocket assumed the shape of a sausage.

There are two ways of operating the oxy-acetylene blowpipe. The first, as recommended by the text books, is to see that the complete joint is clean and well fluxed, then preheat the whole bag of tricks, either with a blowlamp, or the blowpipe itself. Then apply the flame at the beginning of the joint, and when it becomes bright red, hold the end of a welding rod (Sifbronze, or similar) in the flame right over the hot spot, and very close to it. A little blob will melt off the end of the rod, and drop into the joint. Repeat process, but hold the welding rod so that the second drop overlaps the first; then ditto repeat the full length of the joint, so that it presents a rippled appearance. Dip the welding rod in flux at each application. I did plenty that way and they all turned out O.K.

However, there was just one point that didn't satisfy me, viz. that the molten metal did not run right through a lap joint, nor penetrate the full depth of a flanged joint, such as that between the boiler throatplate and the wrapper sheet. To get over this I tried a larger nozzle and lower gas pressure and heated the end of the joint a wee bit above the melting temperature of the welding rod. The latter was then applied in the flame and touching the bright-red metal, so that the end melted off and ran clean into the joint, which it penetrated. The flame was moved slowly along, and the welding rod applied continuously, so that it ran instead of rippling. This did the trick. The nozzle I used for the boiler joints of my *Britannia*-type 4-6-2 is 1/16 in. dia. The boiler is similar to that specified for *Evening Star*. I hope that beginners and other inexperienced workers will find the above information useful; now let us get on with the job.

Smokebox tubeplate

Although the next stage of assembly is fitting the tubes, it will be necessary to make the smokebox tubeplate first, so that it can be used as spacer and support while silversoldering the tubes into the combustion-chamber tubeplate. Saw out a circle of 10-gauge (1/8 in.) sheet copper 5.½ in. dia., well anneal it, and flange it over a former 4.3/8 in. dia. I don't usually bother about cutting out special formers for circular flanged plates, but press into service anything that is handy and of the requisite size, such as an old chuck plate, wheel casting, pulley or similar. Chuck the plate, flange outwards, in the outside jaws of your three-jaw chuck, and face off the ragged edge left by the flanging process; then mount the plate on the outside of the same jaws, gripping by the inside of the flange, and turn the outside of the flange to a tight push fit in the boiler barrel. You can't use the inside jaws for this job, unless the chuck is an outsize one—you'll see why if you try it!

Scribe a line right across the middle of the side opposite to the flange, and another at right angles, at 5/8 in. from the edge. On this line, at 9/32 in. each side of the crossing point, make a good centrepop. Clamp the combustion-chamber tubeplate former to the flanged plate with these two centrepops showing through the two bottom holes in the former. Make sure that the clamp is tight enough to prevent former and plate shifting while drilling, then put the No. 30 drill through the holes in the former, and carry on right through the tubeplate. Remove the former, and open out all the holes as described for the combustion-chamber tubeplate; but this time put the reamers right through the holes, so that the tubes will fit easily. Slightly countersink the holes on both sides; those on the flanged side help to guide the tubes into position when

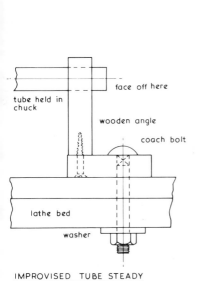

face off here

tube held in chuck

wooden angle

coach bolt

lathe bed

washer

IMPROVISED TUBE STEADY

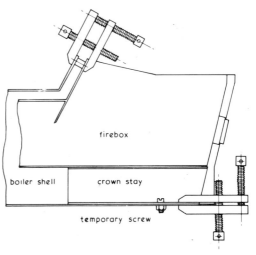

firebox

boiler shell   crown stay

temporary screw

FITTING FIREBOX ASSEMBLY TO BOILER SHELL

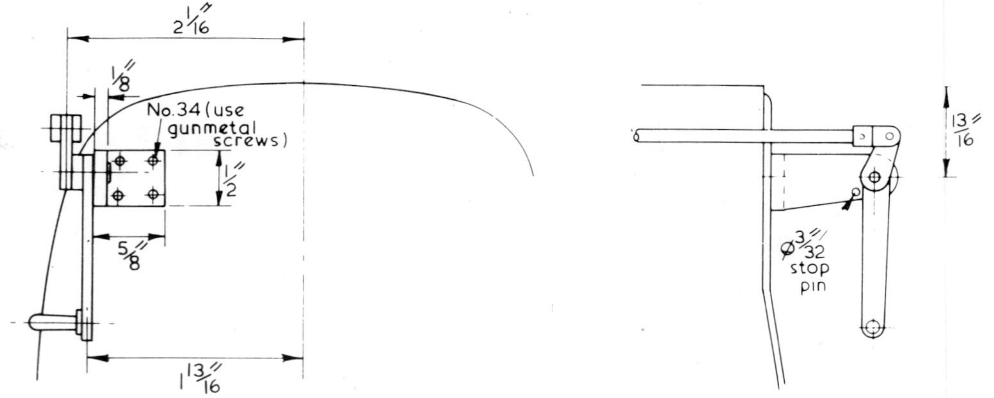

$\varnothing \frac{3}{32}$

$\frac{3}{32}R$

$\varnothing \frac{1}{8}$

$\frac{1}{8}$

$\frac{3}{8}$

$\frac{1}{8}R$

$\frac{3}{8}$

$1\frac{3}{8}$

$\frac{3}{16}$

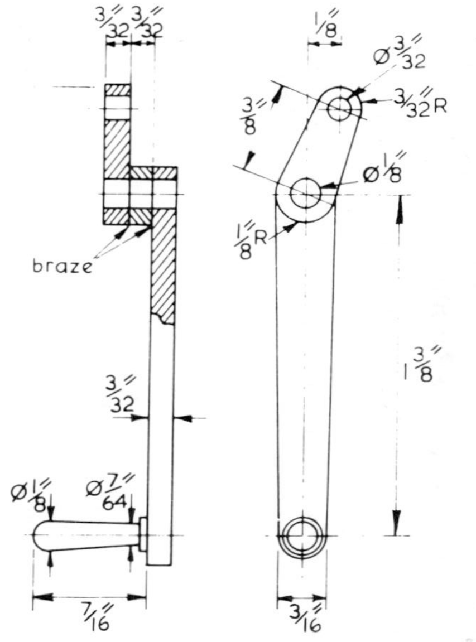

REGULATOR HANDLE: BMS (X2)

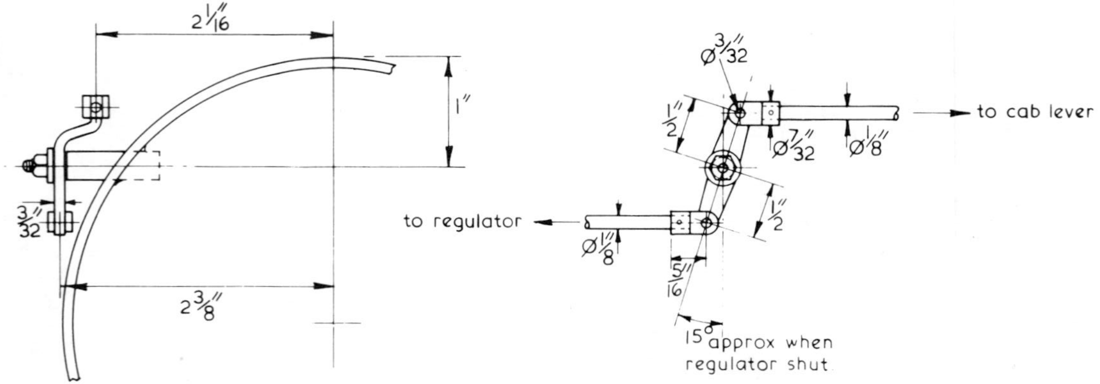

$\frac{3}{32}\ \frac{3}{32}$

braze

$\frac{3}{32}$

$\varnothing \frac{7}{64}$

$\frac{7}{16}$

$\varnothing \frac{1}{8}$

to cab lever

$\frac{1}{8}$

$\varnothing \frac{1}{8}$

$\varnothing \frac{7}{32}$

$\frac{1}{2}$

$\frac{3}{32}$

15° approx when regulator shut

$\frac{1}{2}$

$\frac{5}{16}$

$\varnothing \frac{1}{8}$

to regulator

INTERMEDIATE LEVER FOR REGULATOR (L H S of boiler)

$\frac{13}{16}$

$\varnothing \frac{3}{32}$ stop pin

ARRANGEMENT OF REGULATOR HANDLE 'IN CAB

$2\frac{1}{16}$

No. 34 (use gunmetal screws)

$\frac{1}{2}$

$\frac{1}{8}$

$\frac{5}{8}$

$1\frac{3}{16}$

$1''$

$2\frac{1}{16}$

$2\frac{3}{8}$

$\frac{3}{32}$

fitting the tubeplate, and those on the outside form channels for the silversolder, ensuring a sound job.

On the vertical centreline at $\frac{3}{4}$ in. from the top drill a 7/16 in. hole, and tap it $\frac{1}{2}$ in. × 32 for the steam-pipe flange. To the left, on the same level, drill a 7/32 in. hole and tap it $\frac{1}{4}$ in. × 40 for the blower union nipple. Below these, set out the four holes for the longitudinal stays, drill 9/32 in. and tap 5/16 in. × 40.

Tubes and Flues

Four pieces of $\frac{3}{4}$ in. × 20-gauge seamless copper tube will be required for the superheater flues, and 13 pieces of 7/16 in. × 20-gauge ditto for the firetubes. These must be squared off at the ends, to an overall length of 9.$\frac{1}{4}$ in. Most of the lathes used in home workshops have a hole through the mandrel big enough to admit the smaller size, so the tubes can be pushed in until only $\frac{1}{2}$ in. or so projects from the chuck jaws, and facing off is easy. Don't forget the cutting oil! If the mandrel won't admit the larger tubes, hold the end in the chuck, and support the free end in a steady. If the lathe hasn't one, just nail or screw two

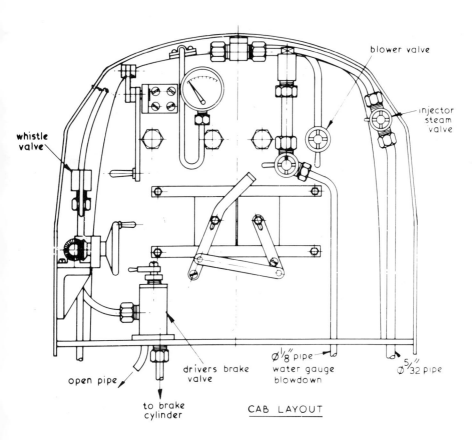

CAB LAYOUT

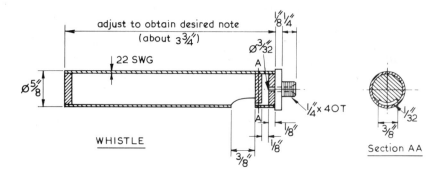

pieces of wood together at right angles, put a $\frac{3}{4}$ in. drill in the chuck or mandrel nose, hold one angle of the wood down tightly to the lathe bed, and press the other against the drill. The drill will soon put a hole through at the correct height! Put a tube in the chuck, put the improvised steady over the end so that about $\frac{1}{2}$ in. projects through the hole, clamp the base part to the lathe bed with a coach bolt and a big washer.

Before removing the tubes from the lathe, clean the ends with coarse emerycloth or similar abrasive, and slightly bevel the ends by holding a second-cut flat file against them while still revolving.

Experienced coppersmiths should have no difficulty in silversoldering the whole nest of tubes into the combustion-chamber tubeplate at one go, but tyros should make a two-stage job of it, doing the four flues and top row of tubes at the first shot, then completing the rest at the second. In the first case, smear plenty of wet flux over the tubeplate before fitting the tube ends. For best-grade silver-solder, use powdered borax mixed to a creamy paste with water. For Easyflo, use the special flux sold for use with it, mixed likewise. Put the tubes through the holes so that a bare 1/16 in. projects inside. Put the smokebox tubeplate on the outer ends, with the tubes coming through about $\frac{1}{4}$ in. or so; it won't slip down, friction will prevent it. Line up the tubes so that they are parallel with the combustion-chamber. Novices follow the same procedure, but put in the four flues and top row of small tubes only.

Stand the assembly in the brazing pan with the tubes pointing skywards, and put on some more flux, pushing it between the tubes with a brush. If doing the lot at once, either cut some sheet silver-solder into 1/8 in. squares, and drop them among the tube ends, or put a ring of silversolder wire around each tube. This must, naturally, be done before putting on the smokebox tubeplate. Two-stagers need not bother about this, as all the ends are accessible. First play the blowlamp flame on the combustion-chamber, and keep it away from the tubes until the tubeplate starts to glow red. Then play on both the tubeplate and tube ends until the whole bag of tricks becomes medium red. When this stage is reached, the bits of silversolder, or rings, as the case may be, will melt and flow all around each tube, making a perfect seal. The blowlamp flame should not be kept playing on the same place, but moved right around the whole nest of tubes, which gives it a chance to get between the tube ends and do the needful to all of them.

Two-stagers go to work in much the same way, heating the combustion-chamber tubeplate first before playing the flame on the tubes; but here, a word of warning. Don't let the flame play on the uncovered holes in the tubeplate for too long, otherwise you'll suddenly find one big ragged hole in place of a lot of little round ones—and that will mean sawing off the tubeplate from the end of the chamber, making and fitting a fresh one, and fitting longer tubes. When tubes and tubeplate grow medium red, apply a strip of best-grade silversolder, or Easyflo wire, to each one. The end will melt off, and run around the tube like water, forming a nice even fillet.

The smokebox ends of the tubes must be softened, so if the lot have been done at one operation, carefully pull off the smokebox tubeplate, and heat the free ends of the tubes to medium red for about 1 in. down. Then put the assembly in the pickle bath for about 15 minutes, after which it should be well washed in running water. Two-stagers should put the job in the pickle-bath without removing the smokebox tubeplate. After washing off, insert the rest of the tubes through the holes in the smokebox tubeplate, fitting the inner ends into the combusion-chamber tubeplate as before. Put plenty of wet flux around

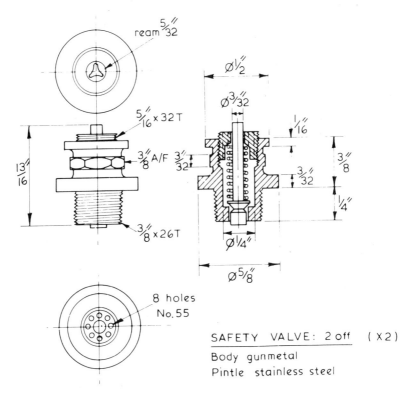

SAFETY VALVE: 2 off   (X2)

Body gunmetal

Pintle stainless steel

them, and repeat the silversoldering operation, as previously described. The second heating won't have the slightest effect on the first, so beginners need have no apprehension whatever. When a fillet of silversolder has run around each tube, remove the smokebox tubeplate, soften the free ends of the tubes as before-mentioned, pickle for 15 minutes and wash off.

Fitting Firebox Assembly to Boiler Shell

Clean the inside of the firebox wrapper and the lower edge of the throatplate between flanges, with coarse emerycloth or similar abrasive. Next, fit the front section of the foundation ring, which is made in four sections from $\frac{1}{4}$ in. square copper rod. Cut a piece to fit tightly between the flanges of the throatplate, slightly rounding the corners on the contact side; clean it well, and jam it in

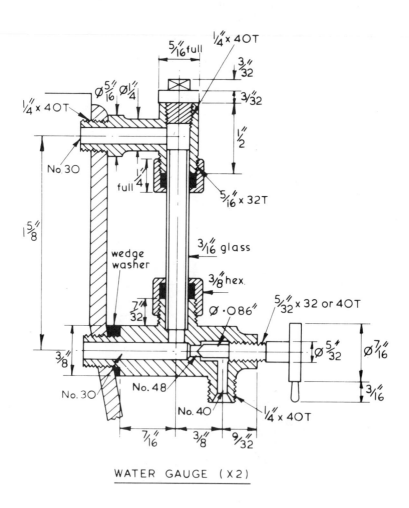

WATER GAUGE (X2)

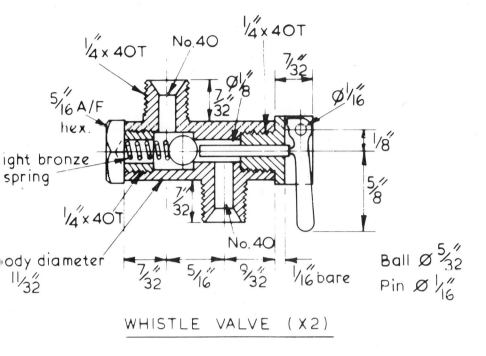

WHISTLE   VALVE   (X2)

place. With the boiler shell upside-down on the bench, slide the firebox and tube assembly into it, until the front of the firebox comes up hard against the pieces of square rod. Set the firebox midway between the wrapper sides, so that the spaces on each side of it are equal, then put a clamp over the lot, to keep the firebox in place, while riveting the crown stays.

The flanges of the crown stays should be in full-length contact with the top of the firebox wrapper. Put a clamp over each, then drill a couple of No. 41 holes through wrapper and each flange, at 1.1/8 in. from the edge of the wrapper and central with the flanges. Put a 7 B.A. screw through each, from the inside of the wrapper, and put a nut on each on the outside, screwing up tightly. These screws will keep the flanges in position when the clamps are removed, and the flanges can then be permanently riveted to the wrapper. Drill through wrapper and flange with No. 41 drill, at $\frac{3}{4}$ in. spacing, keeping the holes in a straight line along the middle of the flange. Scrape off any burring, then put 3/32 in. × 3/8 in. copper rivets through from the inside. To do this easily, I use a strip of 16-gauge steel about $\frac{1}{4}$ in. wide, with a notch in the end like a distant signal. The rivet is jammed in the notch, and is held tight enough to allow the rivet to be poked through the hole from the inside; the projecting shank can then be held on the outside, the notched rod pulled away, and the head of the rivet rested on a dolly. This is a piece of iron bar, about 1 in. × $\frac{1}{2}$ in. section, gripped in the bench vice with about 6 in. projecting from one side. To prevent it slipping while the riveting is under way, I always remove one of the hard steel insets from the vice jaws, and rest the bar on the ledge which supports the inset.

Hold the shank of the rivet, put the boiler over the bar so that the rivet head rests on it, snip off the rivet shank about 1/16 in. from the wrapper, then hammer down the projecting bit to form a head. Repeat operations on each flange, so that there will be four rows of rivets showing through the wrapper. Finally, take out the temporary screws, and put rivets through the holes.

The front section of the foundation ring can then be riveted in. Drill a row of holes with No. 41 drill at $\frac{3}{4}$ in. spacing, and about 1/8 in. from the bottom of the throatplate, right through the outer throatplate, the piece of $\frac{1}{4}$ in. copper bar, and the firebox throatplate. Scrape off any burring inside the firebox, slightly countersink the holes on the outside, and put in 3/32 in. × 5/8 in. roundhead copper rivets, hammering the shanks well down into the countersinks.

Fitting the Smokebox Tubeplate

Clean the inside of the end of the barrel, and insert the smokebox tubeplate, flange first, taking care it is exactly vertical. Tap it in evenly until it barely touches the ends of the tubes. If they line up with the holes, it will be another miracle, but they can easily be coaxed into position by aid of a wooden meat skewer or a blacklead pencil, as the silversoldering job makes them ductile. However, when lining up, be mighty careful to avoid distorting the ends, or

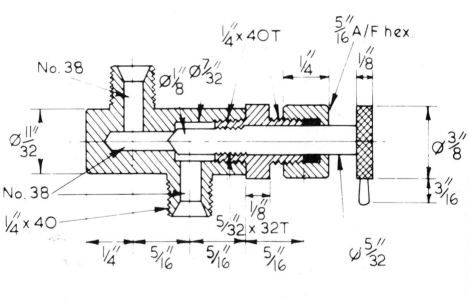

INJECTOR STEAM VALVE (X2)

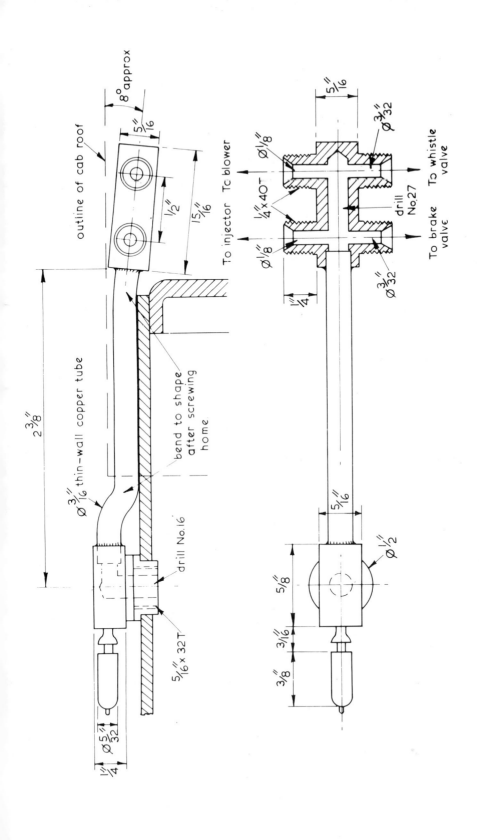

outline of cab roof

8° approx

5/16"

1/2"

15/16"

2 3/8"

Ø 3/16" thin-wall copper tube

bend to shape after screwing home

drill No.16

5/16 x 32T

Ø 5/32"

1/4"

To injector   To blower

To whistle valve

To brake valve

Ø 1/8"

Ø 3/32"

1/4" x 40T

drill No.27

Ø 1/8"

Ø 3/32"

5/16"

1/4"

5/16"

Ø 1/2"

5/8"

3/16"

3/8"

they won't go through the holes. When they are all nicely lined up, carefully tap the tubeplate right home, so that the tubes stand out a bare 1/16 in. from the tubeplate, and the distance from the tubeplate to the end of the barrel is the same all the way around.

The ends of the tubes have now to be expanded into the holes. This is done with a taper drift; the taper shank of a worn-out or broken drill is just the tool for the job. Grease it, insert it into the tube end, and hit gently with a hammer until the tube is forced tightly against the hole. If the drift sticks and doesn't want to come out, a sideways tap will teach it good manners.

Smear some wet flux all around the joint between barrel and tubeplate flange, around the tube ends, and along the four crownstay flanges. Get a tray of some sort about 1 ft. square or round—the lid of a biscuit tin would do—and cut a hole in it 4.$\frac{3}{4}$ in. dia. to fit over the boiler barrel. Stand the boiler on end, and put the tray over it, about 3 in. from the top, propping it up with a couple of bricks, or something similar, to prevent it from slipping down while the job is under way. Pile some small coke or breeze in the tray, all around the barrel, to the level of the tubeplate, and get the blowpipe going good and strong.

Use either easy-running brazing-strip or coarse-grade silversolder for the circumferential joint. Play the flame all over the tubeplate and barrel end until they are well heated, then concentrate on that part of the joint farthest away from the tubes. As soon as it glows bright red—the coke will help—apply the strip, and when it melts and flows in, work your way steadily right around the barrel, directing the flame partly inside and partly outside, until you get a nice even fillet between barrel and tubeplate. Next direct the flame on the tube ends (watch your step here, to avoid burning them) and when they and the surrounding metal becomes medium red, apply a strip of best-grade silversolder, or Easyflo, to each. As this melts at low temperature it will "flash" around each tube, filling the countersinks and making a perfect seal.

Now, some quick action is called for. Take the tray off the barrel, grip the boiler with the big tongs, holding by the throatplate—mind it doesn't slip!—and lay it in the brazing pan with the firebox overhanging the edge. Put a brick or something else fairly heavy, on the barrel, to prevent the whole issue from tipping over. Play the blowlamp flame on the firebox wrapper from the under- neath, until it glows red, then blow on the crownstay flanges inside the wrapper, until the whole back end of the boiler is red. Then feed in a strip of best-grade silversolder, or Easyflo, the full length of each crownstay flange, and keep the heat on until the melted metal has sweated full length between flanges and wrapper.

If possible, enlist the services of an assistant with another blowpipe on this job. The assistant should play the flame on the outside of the wrapper, while the operator directs his flame on the inside, along the flanges. Literally caught between two fires, the metal will rapidly heat to the required temperature, and the silversolder will melt and penetrate in fine style, sealing all the rivets.

The completed model of the "Evening Star" built by R H Proctor of Twyford, Berks   (photograph by Lorna Minton)

CHAPTER THIRTEEN

"Martin Evans now takes up the story"

The late LBSC left us at a fairly late stage in the construction of the *Evening Star* boiler, having shown readers how to assemble the inner firebox and combustion chamber, complete with tubes, in the outer wrapper/barrel, with the smokebox tubeplate brazed in, and the firebox crownstays brazed to the outer wrapper. The next step therefore is to prepare the backhead, and fit the two side sections of the foundation ring.

The backhead is made from 1/8 in. or 3 mm. copper sheet, a piece about $5\frac{3}{4}$ in. square being required; after flanging over the former, as described in the previous chapters, mark out the position of the four tapped holes, three of which are tapped 5/16 in. × 40t. for the longitudinal stays, and the one on the right 3/8 in. × 40t. for the blower. Mark out also the tapped holes for the water gauge, these are $\frac{1}{4}$ in. × 40t. and are situated 7/8 in. to the right of the vertical centre-line, with the upper hole $\frac{1}{4}$ in. from the top and the lower hole I 5/8 in. below. Although LBSC did not specify bushes for backhead fittings, I would strongly recommend the fitting of gunmetal bushes for all fittings that would

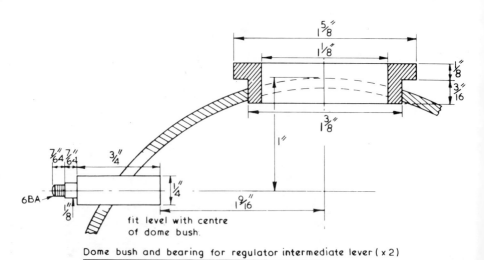

Dome bush and bearing for regulator intermediate lever (x 2)

(gunmetal)

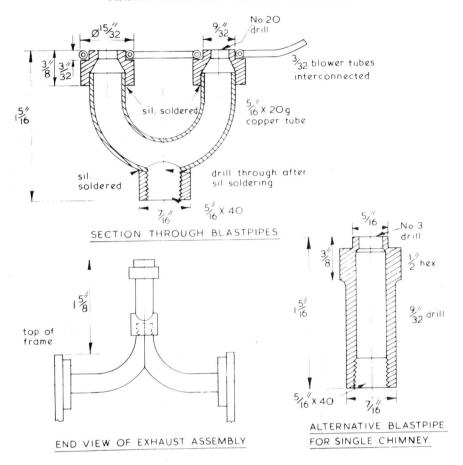

SECTION THROUGH BLASTPIPES

END VIEW OF EXHAUST ASSEMBLY

ALTERNATIVE BLASTPIPE
FOR SINGLE CHIMNEY.

otherwise have to be screwed directly in the boiler. Gunmetal bushes not only give one a greater number of threads, but the material takes threads better than copper. Furthermore, it makes possible the re-drilling and tapping of the holes, should this ever be necessary in the life of the boiler. For the water gauge and similar boiler fittings, the bushes could be turned from 3/8 in. gunmetal, reduced to 5/16 in. leaving a "head" for flange about 1/16 in. thick, with a total thickness of $\frac{1}{4}$ in. This is for bushes tapped $\frac{1}{4}$ in. × 40t. other bushes in proportion.

Note that after flanging, the backhead has to be bent at a point 1.1/16 in. from the top, to match the outer wrapper; this means that the lower water gauge bush (and the firedoor) will be at an angle, so the bottom fitting of the water gauge will need a "wedge washer". Cut out the firehole, checking its position from the firehole tube projecting from the firebox backplate; aim for a snug fit.

The side sections of the foundation ring are cut from $\frac{1}{4}$ in. square copper, also the back section. Chamfer the bottom edges of these before assembling, as this leaves a useful gap to assist penetration of the silversolder.

Having fitted the bushes to the backhead, braze them with B.6 or L.7 brazing alloy, which melts at a temperature considerably higher than Easyflo or Easyflo No. 2, which I suggest be used for the final brazing job; alternately, C.4 or LX.13 may be used, this melts at about 740 deg. C. Now fit the backhead in place, together with the side and end pieces of the foundation ring. Two 3/32 in. copper rivets will hold the backhead, so turn up a few 6 BA screws from drawn gunmetal, and use these, drilling through firebox outer wrapper and the flange of the backhead with No. 42 drill, then opening out the wrapper only with No. 34 drill. Tap 6 BA with great care as it is very easy to break these small taps in copper work. The gunmetal screws will pull the wrapper into close contact with the backhead, and we can then lightly pein over the firehole ring where it protrudes through the backhead, resting the boiler on the inner end of the ring on a stout bar of steel held in the vice. We are then ready for the final and biggest brazing operation, apart from the few bushes that we have yet to fit to the barrel etc.

It requires quite a lot of heat to raise the temperature of the foundation ring, and particularly the backhead and firehole ring, for brazing the joints, so I

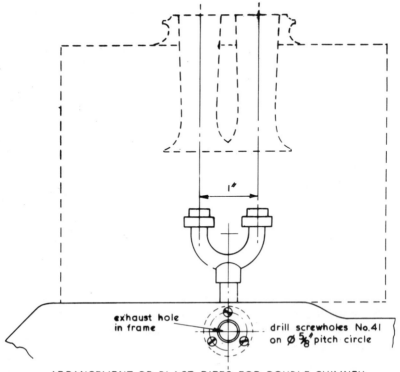

ARRANGEMENT OF BLAST PIPES FOR DOUBLE CHIMNEY

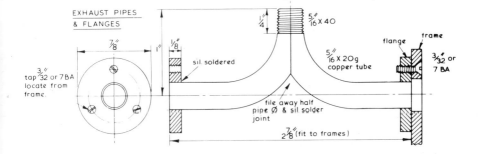

strongly recommend the use of Easyflo No. 2 here, as this is the silversolder with the lowest melting point on the market.

I expect most builders of *Evening Star* will be using one of the popular propane blowpipes for the brazing operations on the boiler. If so, they will find one of the very large ones (such as Sievert No. 2944) gives enough heat for the next operation, BUT, and it is a very big but! this size of burner gives such a large flame that it becomes very difficult to see what is going on, whether the silversolder is flowing in the right places etc, etc. Also, the great amount of heat very close to the operators' hands makes life rather difficult, to say the least. I would therefore strongly recommend that builders obtain the help of a friend, holding another blowpipe, in which case it would be better to use two of the next smaller burners—No. 2943.

We want to be able to braze both the foundation ring and the backhead consecutively, so that the boiler has no chance to cool down in the middle of the job. The builder should therefore be prepared to stand the boiler up on its end, with the backhead pointing skyward, immediately the foundation ring has been finished, so the tray with the large hole cut in it mentioned by LBSC in the last chapter will be required. But first lay the boiler down on its back in the brazing pan and pile the coke all around to within ¾ in. or so of the foundation ring. Also stuff some asbestos cubes or sheet inside the firebox, covering the combustion chamber and fill the inside with more small coke, keeping it well away from the foundation ring. Flux well, and play the blowpipe flame/s all around the foundation ring until the whole is glowing dull red. Then feed in Easyflo No. 2, going all around, and forming a nice fillet. I should have mentioned earlier that if after fitting the sections of the foundation ring there were any small gaps left, these must be filled up by driving in slivers of copper, otherwise the silversolder would run straight through the gaps. Now pull up the boiler with the big tongs, and set it up in the tray with the hole in it and pile up the coke all around to within an inch or so of the backhead. Flux thoroughly and get the blowpipes going strongly again. Work all around the backhead, then concentrate the heat on the firehole ring, forming a nice fillet all around this. Allow the boiler to cool sufficiently so that it can be handled safely, and put into the pickle for at least 20 minutes.

All we need now is to fit the remaining bushes and the bearing for the intermediate lever for the regulator, if these have not been dealt with before. Easyflo No. 2 is the best here. We can now carry out a preliminary test, before fitting the stays. Turn up some threaded plugs, to fit all the bushes or tapped holes, except for two, which we will need for the attachment of the test pressure gauge and a connection for the hand pump. The plugs can be made in brass, with the threads left a shade on the tight side. Screw them home with a taste of plumber's jointing on the threads and attach a test pressure gauge to one of the safety-valve bushes, but NOT the miniature pressure gauge that is to be used for the engine itself! A large gauge reading up to at least 300 p.s.i. is essential for boiler testing. The hand pump can be placed in a tray containing water and connected to the lower water gauge bush in the backhead.

Fill the boiler with water, excluding all air, and pump away with the hand pump until the pressure gauge reads 20 p.s.i. Don't go any higher, as the boiler is as yet unstayed, and any higher pressure might cause some of the flat parts to bulge. If any leaks show up, deal with these before proceeding further. Even experienced boiler makers sometimes find a small leak or two at this stage, but they are nothing to worry about, simply drill a No. 55 hole at the offending spot, tap 10 BA and screw in a stub of copper wire with a smear of plumber's jointing on the threads. Should the builder be really unlucky and find a leak somewhere

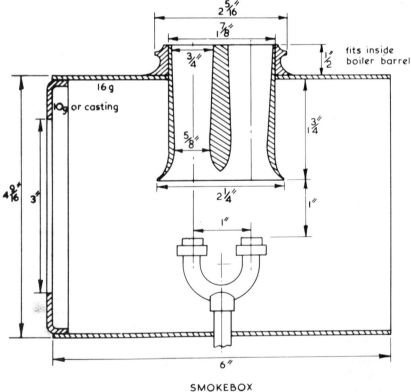

SMOKEBOX

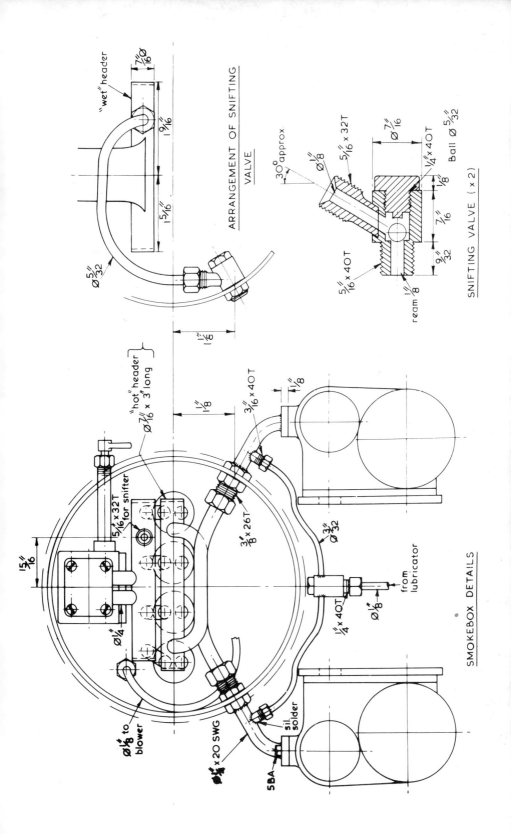

ARRANGEMENT OF SNIFTING
VALVE

"wet" header

7/16" Ø

9/16"

15/16"

Ø 5/32"

SNIFTING VALVE (× 2)

30° approx

Ø 1/8"

5/16 × 32T

7/16" Ø

1/4 × 4OT

Ball Ø 5/32"

1/8"

7/16"

9/32"

ream 1/8"

5/16 × 4OT

SMOKEBOX DETAILS

15/16"

5/16 × 32T for snifter

Ø 1/4"

Ø 1/8" to blower

"hot" header
Ø 7/16" × 3" long

1/8"

3/16 × 4OT

3/8 × 26T

3/32" Ø

1/8"

1/4 × 4OT

Ø 1/8"

from lubricator

× 2O SWG

sil. solder

5BA

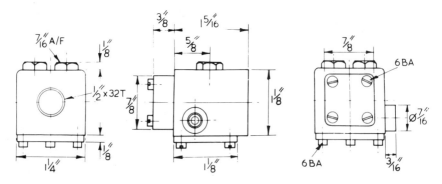

POPPET VALVE REGULATOR : body gunmetal

in the combustion chamber that is quite inaccessible, probably the only solution is to put a quantity of high-melting point soft solder inside the boiler, together with a good dose of the appropriate flux, heat the whole boiler up to the melting point of this solder, and "Swish" the boiler around in the hope that some of the solder will find the gap and fill it—not an ideal solution perhaps, but this may be why combustion chambers are not too popular among model engineers today!

Boiler Stays

We could fit the longitudinal stays first. The three solid ones can be made from 3/16 in. drawn gunmetal, or better still from monel metal which can be obtained from M.E. advertisers. This is threaded 40t. at each end and fitting is by means of "blind nipples", threaded 5/16 in. × 40t. outside and 3/16 in. × 40t inside.

LBSC had a useful tip on how to get these stays through the tapped holes at each end of the boiler. He used a thin-walled tube that would pass through the tapped holes and about 3 in. longer than the boiler, inserting this from the smokebox end. The end of the stay rod was then put in the end of the tube and pushed right home, the nipple being screwed into the backhead. The tube was then pulled out at the smokebox end, when the end of the stay was found to be in the tapped hole in the smokebox tubeplate, when the second nipple was screwed home, locking the stay firmly to the tubeplate.

The blower stay is fitted in the same way, this being $\frac{1}{4}$ in. copper tube with thick walls—say 1/8 in. bore. The nipple is threaded 3/8 in. × 40t. and $\frac{1}{4}$ in. × 40t. Only one is required and this is a "special" having a union connection for the blower, as shown on the drawings. At the backhead end, the blower valve is screwed home in place of a normal nipple.

Next, we require six transverse stays, again 3/16 in. dia. and threaded 40t at each end. The nipples are similar to the "blind" ones on the long stays, but due to the sloping sides of the firebox, "wedge" washers will be needed on each side, so file up 12 of these from a scrap piece of 3/32 in. or 2 mm. copper sheet, and drill them 3/16 in. dia. These transverse stays can be fed in from either side and are locked in place as for the long stays.

LBSC showed 5 BA firebox stays on his original drawings, 8 of them at the throatplate, 14 between the firebox backplate and the backhead, and 39 on each side of the firebox, a total of 102 stays. He also specified copper for these stays. However, builders will find drawn gunmetal much easier to thread than copper and also considerably stronger. Further, we can cut down the number of these stays quite a bit, especially if we use 4 BA rather than 5 BA. It will be appreciated that a 4 BA stay in gunmetal is much stronger than a 5 BA copper one. What I would suggest is that the top two rows of side stays have seven 4 BA

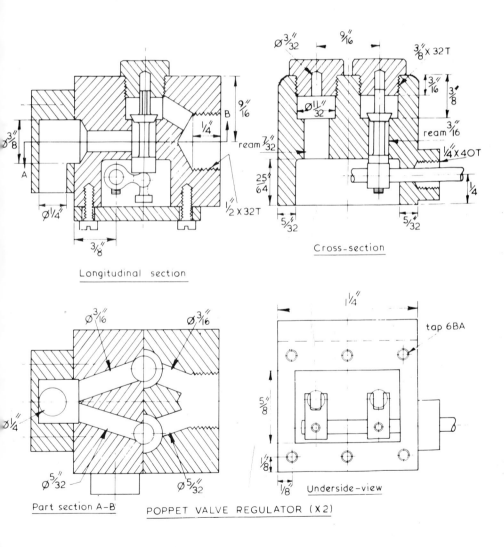

Longitudinal section

Cross-section

Part section A-B   POPPET VALVE REGULATOR (X2)

Underside-view

Valves 6O inc. angle

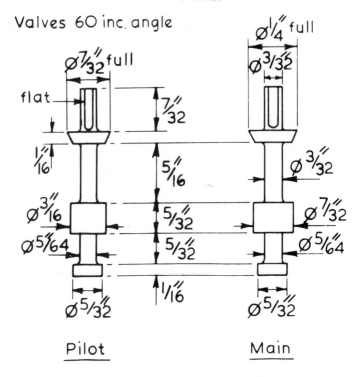

Pilot   Main

REGULATOR VALVES: Stainless steel (x2)

stays, equispaced, the next two rows also have 7 stays, and the bottom row 6 instead of 7.

Again, the number of stays in the throatplates can be reduced to 5, in a single row, the two shown on the drawing being so close to the barrel that they are not necessary. At the backhead, we will have to stick to the two on each side of the firehole ring, but the two rows of six underneath the firehole can be reduced to two rows of 5 each; thus the total number of stays is reduced to 87.

However, whether builders prefer to stick to 5 BA stays or to fit 4 BA, the process of fitting them is exactly the same. Mark out their positions as carefully as possible, centrepop at each point, but not too hard as the copper will be very soft after brazing operations, and drill right through both outer and inner plates—No. 40 for 5 BA stays, or No. 33 for 4 BA. Take care to keep the drill at right angles to the plates, and where the angle of the inner and outer plates is slightly different, for instance at the top row of side stays, aim to have the drill at right-angles to the *inner* plate. Tap with a special staybolt tap if available—this type of tap has a pilot pin which helps to guide the tap truly—and use a little cutting oil which will help to ensure clean threads; but copper is not a nice metal to thread!

If using copper for the stays, these can be lightly riveted over on the outside,

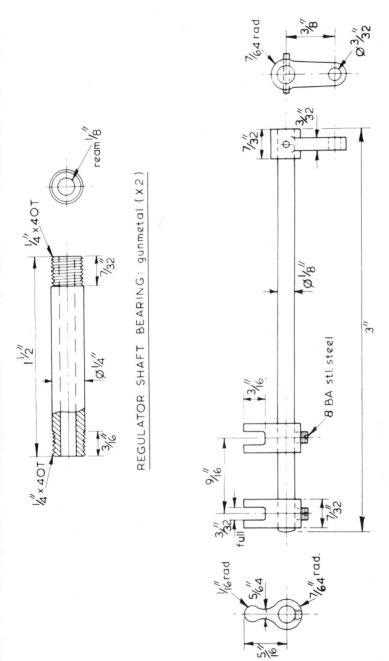

REGULATOR SHAFT BEARING: gunmetal (X2)

ream ⅛"

¼" x 40T

1½"

⌀¼"

7/32"

3/16"

¼" x 40T

REGULATOR SHAFT & LEVERS: shaft stainless steel
inside levers gunmetal
outside lever b.m s.

7/64 rad.

3/8"

⌀3/32"

3/32"

7/32"

⌀⅛"

3"

8 BA stl. steel

3/16"

9/16"

3/32" full

7/32"

⅛"rad

5/64"

7/64"rad.

5/16"

but if using gunmetal, don't risk riveting, as this metal being harder and tougher than copper, the plate may be damaged. For a 4 BA stay, use 3/16 in. dia. gunmetal rod; put a length in the 3-jaw, turn down enough length to 0.142 in. dia. for one stay and thread 4 BA, then *partly* part off the rod to give a half-round head of about 1/16 in. thickness and remove the rod from the chuck. We can now screw this stay right home in the boiler, and then twist off the rest of the rod, which is then re-chucked for the next stay. If using copper, there is no need to choose a larger diameter than the thread outside diameter, 1/8 in. being near enough for 5 BA. The copper stay is screwed home and nutted on the inside, about 3/32 in. being left projecting from the outside, this being riveted over to a neat rounded head, the nut on the inside being supported on a stout steel bar held in the vice.

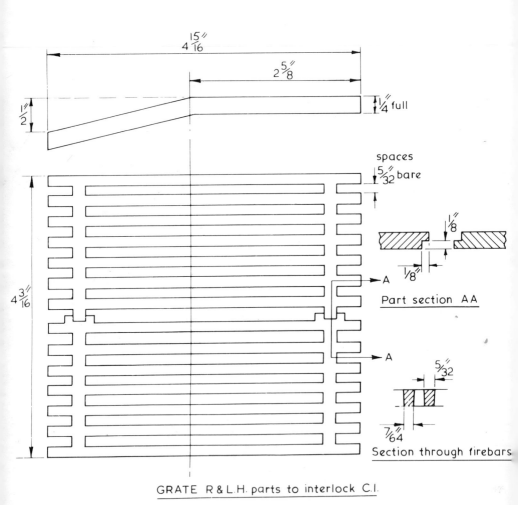

GRATE R & L.H. parts to interlock C.I.

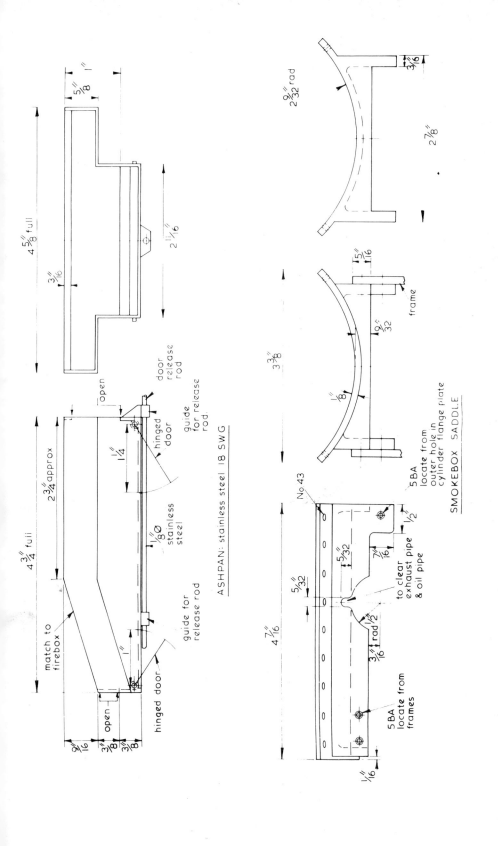

ASHPAN: stainless steel 18 SWG

SMOKEBOX SADDLE

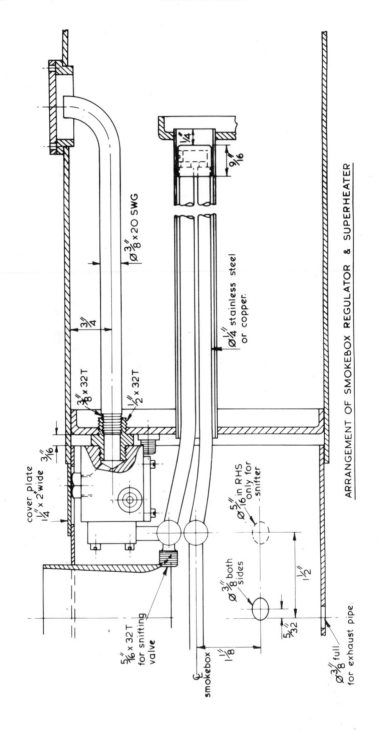

ARRANGEMENT OF SMOKEBOX REGULATOR & SUPERHEATER

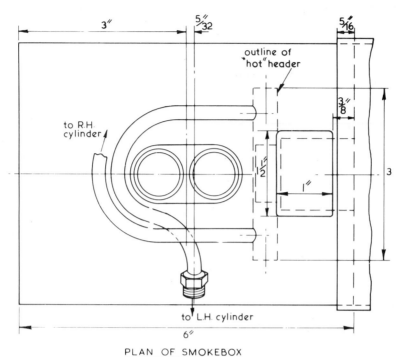

3"

5/32

5/16

outline of
"hot" header

to R.H.
cylinder

3/8"

1/2"

1"

3

to L.H. cylinder

6"

PLAN OF SMOKEBOX
To show opening for regulator & steam pipes to cylinders

Incidentally, although ordinary commercial brass nuts can be used on the inside of the firebox, a better idea is to use brass "dome" nuts; these being "blind", there is rather less chance of leakage than with ordinary nuts.

The stays will now have to be sweated over to prevent leakage. It is essential to use a soft solder with a higher melting point than that of the ordinary commercial "plumber's" or "tinman's" solder; "Comsol" can be recommended. The whole boiler should be heated up to the melting point of the solder, and the stay nuts and heads well fluxed with "Comsol" flux, the solder can then be applied to every stay head and nut, both inside and outside the firebox, forming a little fillet over each. Allow the boiler to cool slowly after this treatment, then wash thoroughly to remove all traces of the flux; we will then be ready for the final hydraulic test.

The hydraulic test is exactly as described for the preliminary test, except that the pressure is taken up to twice working pressure, which in this case is 160 p.s.i. (the working pressure of the boiler being 80 p.s.i.). Be careful to ensure that all air is excluded from the boiler, and keep the pressure at 160 for at least ten minutes. If all is well, the test equipment can be dismantled and the boiler passed for service.

Perhaps I should mention, at this stage, that all model engineering societies now insist on proper boiler testing before locomotives are permitted to run in public, so the builder will be well advised to have his boiler tested by officials of his nearest society. Even if he is not a member of such a society, most club members are willing to help "lone hands"!

Smokebox Saddle

I was hoping that the saddle specified for LBSC's *Britannia* could be used, as there is only a sixteenth or so difference in the diameters of the two smokeboxes, but it was not to be, due to the fact that *Evening Star's* cylinders are very steeply inclined.

It is always a big advantage in any model locomotive to be able to assemble or dismantle the smokebox saddle without disturbing the cylinders, and most builders will already have their cylinders bolted to the frames by the time they start thinking about the saddle. After much thought, I came to the conclusion that a very long saddle would be the answer, as in any case it will be almost entirely hidden by the smoke deflectors and the running boards. The long saddle enables us to get a couple of screws in, just ahead of the cylinder flange plate, so the first thing to do is to drill two no. 30 holes in the frames, at 5/32 in. below the top edge, one to be $2\frac{1}{2}$ in. from the extreme front end of the frame, and the other 7/16 in. to the rear of the first. 5 BA hexagon-head bolts can then be used through these holes into tapped holes in the saddle. At the rear end, the hole in the extreme right top corner of the cylinder flange plate can be utilised, a longer bolt being used through this plate, through the frame and into another tapped hole in the rear lug of the saddle. Thus six 5 BA bolts are used to hold down the saddle and this should be ample.

The smokebox will of course have been previously fitted to the boiler barrel before the saddle is taken in hand. Incidentally, on *Evening Star*, the smokebox fits *inside* the boiler barrel, being 4.9/16 in. dia. as against $4\frac{3}{4}$ in. dia. for the barrel. It should be a good fit, and to ensure air-tightness, it is a good idea to smear the join with plumber's jointing before assembly. The barrel should overlap the smokebox by 3/8 in. Either a row of small countersunk steel screws may be used, to make a strong joint, or rivets may be put in, in which case use 1/16 in. or even 3/64 in. copper or brass snaphead.

The smokebox is held to the saddle by a row of 8 BA hexagon-head screws on each side, and when drilling the saddle, it is probably wise to have the smokebox previously bolted down to the saddle, so that the boiler as a whole can be set level.

The Regulator

On LBSC's original boiler drawing, no provision was made for the usual bush or tapped hole in the upper part of the backhead. He did however show a tubular bearing fitted to the left-hand side of the barrel in line with the dome

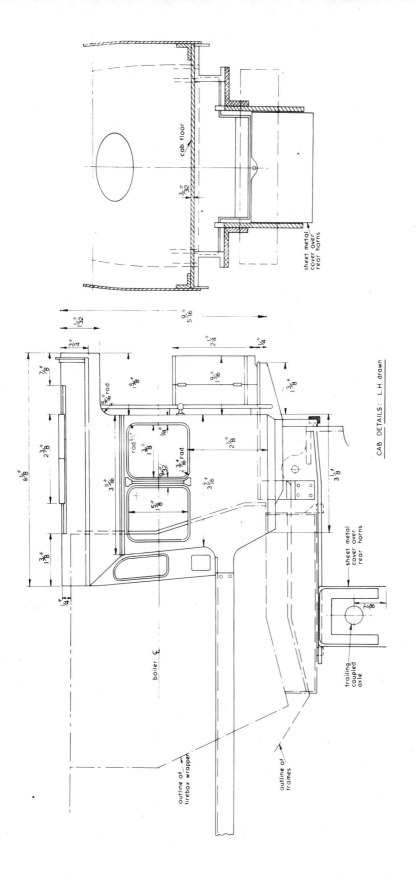

cab floor

$\frac{3}{32}$"

sheet metal
cover over
rear horns

CAB DETAILS: L.H. drawn

$\frac{1}{32}$"

$\frac{9}{16}$"

$\frac{3}{4}$"

$2\frac{1}{4}$"

$\frac{1}{4}$"

$\frac{7}{8}$"

$\frac{5}{8}$"

$\frac{9}{16}$"

$1\frac{3}{8}$"

$\frac{5}{16}$" rad

rad $\frac{1}{4}$"

$\frac{1}{4}$"

$2\frac{3}{8}$"

rad $\frac{1}{2}$"

$\frac{3}{8}$"

$2\frac{1}{8}$"

$6\frac{1}{8}$"

$\frac{3}{8}$"

$\frac{3}{16}$" rad.

$\frac{9}{32}$"

$\frac{11}{16}$"

$\frac{3}{4}$"

$3\frac{1}{16}$"

$3\frac{1}{8}$"

$5\frac{1}{8}$"

$1\frac{3}{8}$"

$\frac{1}{4}$"

sheet metal
cover over
rear horns

boiler 3

$\frac{7}{8}$"

trailing
coupled
axle

outline of
firebox wrapper

outline of
frames

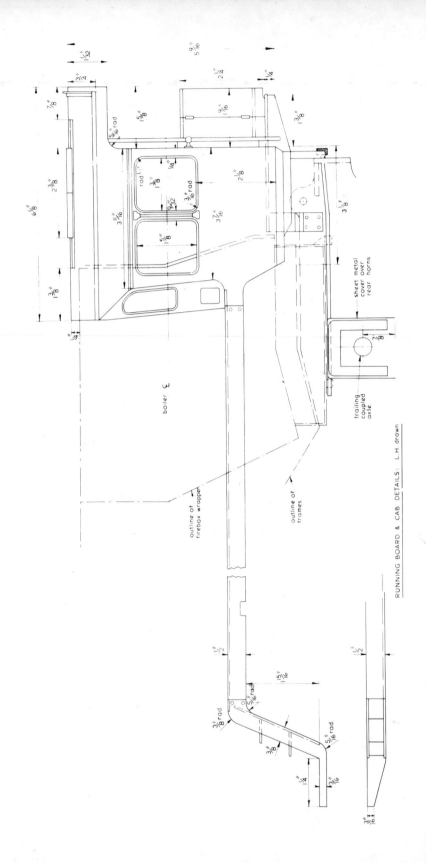

RUNNING BOARD & CAB DETAILS: L.H drawn

and a short distance below the top of the barrel. Possibly his intention was to specify a slide valve type regulator in the dome, similar to the alternative regulator on *Britannia*, but to operate this from outside the boiler barrel.

The trouble with this type of regulator is that the operating spindle, which protrudes from the boiler, is under boiler pressure at all times, so needs a reliable stuffing box. Furthermore, this spindle can only operate on one side of the valve, so that as soon as any wear develops, the valve tends to be moved with a twisting motion, which is not good at all.

My first thought was to specify a conventional regulator in the dome, but apart from alterations to the backhead, there is insufficient height in the *Evening Star* dome to make this a practical solution. Another idea was to fit one of the disc-in-a-tube type, so that the dome would be merely an ornament, but disc-in-a-tube regulators have the reputation of a tendency to leak steam when shut.

Eventually, I came to the conclusion that a multiple valve poppet type regulator, situated in the smokebox, was the answer, and a close look at LBSC's design of this type for his *Britannia* decided me. The body of this could be made out of a piece of $1\frac{1}{4}$ in. square gunmetal or Naval brass, with the valves in stainless steel, and although there is rather more work in a regulator of this type, it should be a fascinating thing to make. My drawings show a regulator almost identical to LBSC's design, apart from some details—for instance, the body has been made a shade longer in order to allow a longer thread where the regulator screws on to the steam pipe extension; the little forked levers have been made longer, so that they bear against the centre of the valve extensions rather than on their edges, which would tend to push the valves slightly to one side. These forked levers have also been furnished with grub screws, so that they can be fixed to their shaft after assembly inside the recess in the regulator body. The steam passages to the pilot valve and from pilot valve to the superheater header have been reduced to 5/32 in. diameter, rather than 3/16 in., as the smaller passages will pass all the steam necessary, in view of the fact that when the main valve opens, the pilot valve stays open too, giving a combined cross-sectional area of 0.0468 sq. in., almost as much as the bore of the main steam pipe.

When making the body of the poppet valve regulator, after finishing to the correct length, width and height, the two vertical holes for the valves should be drilled and reamed right through, the body being held in the 4-jaw chuck with the usual precautions as to squareness etc. Without shifting in the chuck, these holes can then be opened out with drills and D-bits, to form the valve seats, afterwards tapping 3/8 in. × 32t.

The regulator body is removed from the chuck for end-milling out the recess at the bottom. It is then returned to the chuck for drilling for the steam pipe, this being drilled to a depth of not more than $\frac{1}{4}$ in. The hole can be tapped just far enough to enable the tap to be used later by hand, after the two holes have been drilled upwards at an angle to meet the valve chamber. This method will avoid damaging the $\frac{1}{2}$ in. thread. The body is once again reversed in the chuck to

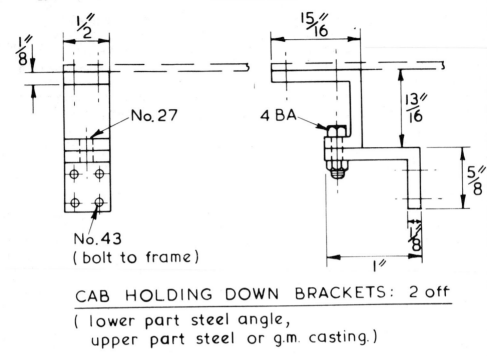

CAB HOLDING DOWN BRACKETS: 2 off

(lower part steel angle,
upper part steel or g.m. casting.)

drill from the other side, 3/8 in. dia. not deeper than 1/32 in., then the two holes, one 3/16 in. and one 5/32 in. diameter, are drilled at an angle, as shown, to break into the valve recesses.

If a casting has been used for the regulator body, the 7/16 in. dia. boss on the right-hand side can now be machined and at the same setting, a 1/8 in. dia hole drilled and reamed into the bottom recess, for the operating spindle. This hole is then opened out for a depth of a shade over 3/16 in. and tapped $\frac{1}{4}$ in. × 40t.

The caps which seal off the valve chambers and also act as guides for the valves will need careful machining, to ensure that the 3/32 in. dia. holes are truly concentric; it might be worth screw-cutting their 3/8 in. × 32t. threads.

The valves are machined from stainless steel, and they require to be a really good fit in their respective bores, but without any suspicion of tightness, otherwise the pressure of the steam will not be sufficient to keep the valves on their seats when the regulator is shut.

As regards the operating spindle, the outer lever can be permanently pinned to this, but the two forked levers, which actuate the valves, will require grub screws, so that they can be assembled in their recess after the spindle has been slid home. Note that the two levers must not be in line, but the lever which actuates the pilot valve should be arranged slightly higher than the other—a difference in angle of about 5 degrees should do nicely—so that the pilot valve opens before the main valve.

It is of course most important that the two forked levers should not work loose on the operating spindle. Having determined their exact position on the shaft, therefore, dimples should be made in the shaft and the grub screws tightened into them. The grub screws should be made in stainless steel and their threads made on the tight side. To make doubly sure of things, these levers could be pinned as well; as even 1/16 in. dia. pins would weaken the spindle appreciably, the shanks of H.S.S. drills could be used instead—No. 56 would be about right. The spindle and levers could be taken out of the regulator for pinning, the dimples in the spindle being sufficient to locate the levers in their correct positions, and the grub screws used to hold them firmly while drilling; on re-assembling the spindle and levers in the regulator, the pins could be inserted from underneath and driven home with a light hammer, the spindle being supported by jamming a strip of brass or something similar above the bosses of the levers.

The regulator is connected to the "wet" header by an extension piece, 7/8 in. square × 3/8 in. thick, bolted on as shown. This is drilled ¼ in. dia. for two short lengths of copper tube running into the "wet" header, which consists of a 2 & 7/8 in. length of 7/16 in. dia. copper tube. This carries a 5/16 in. × 32t. union for a pipe to the snifting valve, which is located in the right-hand side of the smokebox.

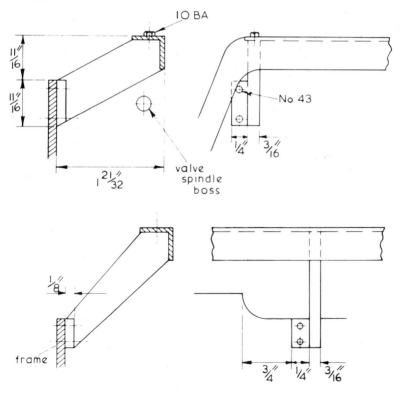

RUNNING BOARD BRACKETS: 2 off each type   B.M.S.   L.H. & R.H.

Stainless steel tube is used for the superheater elements, though as these are much shorter than usual, ending just short of the combustion chamber, copper tube could be used if preferred.

The "hot" header consists of another piece of the 7/16 in. dia. tube, this time 3 in. long, and from this we have the $\frac{1}{4}$ in. × 20 s.w.g. copper tubes to the cylinders, via 3/8 in. × 26t. unions inside the smokebox. The outside steam pipes carry 3/16 in. × 40t. unions for the oil pipes from the mechanical lubricator.

Reverting to the regulator again, it may be asked how the main steam pipe inside the boiler can be assembled. It should be easy enough to get it through the inner dome bush, but the problem may be to hold it firmly while screwing home the connecting piece (which connects the regulator body to the steam pipe). One method which should be satisfactory, is to jam a coarse square file in the upturned end of the pipe. If this distorts the end of the tube it won't matter in the least!

Continuing with the regulator, an intermediate lever is now required, approximately halfway between the regulator body and the cab lever or handle. It is situated in line with the dome, supported by a short stub of $\frac{1}{4}$ in. dia. gunmetal silversoldered into the barrel, and it is set over quite a bit to keep the control rodding close to the barrel. The forked joints can be cut from 3/16 in. square mild steel for neatness, with 3/32 in. dia. pins.

The regulator handle is a simple job, cut from mild or stainless steel, and it is supported on a piece of brass angle, 1/8 in. thick, which in turn is bolted to the backhead. Bronze or gunmetal screws should be used here, and take extra care when tapping the backhead—a broken tap in a boiler backhead is a minor disaster, to say the least! A stop pin is required in this angle, arranged so that the regulator handle is vertical when the regulator is shut. If the pin is put in first, adjustment can be made by the length of the rodding.

Reversing Gear

The reach rod and cab reverser can be tackled now. The reach rod is a length of 3/16 in. dia. mild, silver or stainless steel, turned down to 1/8 in. dia. at the cab end, and at the front end, tapped internally 5 BA for a depth of about 3/8 in. Universal joints are required at each end of the reach rod, these being machined from 5/16 in. square b.m.s. After drilling the cross holes 0.071 in. dia., the "jaw" or forked components are slotted 3/16 in. wide. A short piece of steel of this thickness is then inserted into the jaw so that the job can be held in the 4-jaw chuck for turning the other end, and drilling 1/8 in. dia. The "spider" is turned from 3/16 in. dia. b.m.s., down to 0.182 in. dia. to give a little clearance in the jaw. It is then cross drilled and tapped 10 BA right through at 90 deg. The pins, turned down to 0.070 in. dia., are threaded 10 BA and given screwdriver slots for each assembly. All these parts could be made in silver steel, stainless steel, or b.m.s. case-hardened, as preferred. See pages 116–120.

The cab reverser utilises a pair of 3/8 in. bevel gears, these being as supplied for LBSC's *Britannia*. The reverser is mounted on a short length of brass angle, 1/8 in. thick, which in turn is riveted to the left-hand cab side, six 1/16 in. snaphead rivets being used for the sake of good appearance. There is no need to use screws here, as the bracket carrying the bearings for the handwheel and bevel shafts is held down by 6 and 8 BA screws, as shown.

Coming now to some of the boiler fittings, the two safety valves are similar to those described by LBSC, and are made from 5/8 in. dia. gunmetal. Perhaps the best way to machine these is to turn down the bottom end to 3/8 in. dia., thread 26t. or to suit the boiler bushes, then make a tapped bush to suit, and while this is still in the lathe, each safety valve in turn can be screwed into this; centre and drill right through with No. 24 drill and ream 5/32 in. dia. Then open out with $\frac{1}{4}$ in. drill and bottom with a D-bit, tapping 5/16 in. × 32t at the top (tapping drill

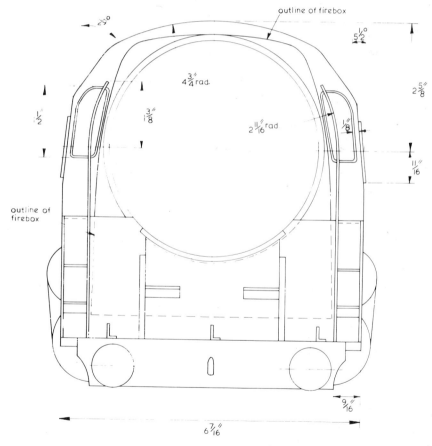

END ELEVATION: To show spectacle plate & smoke deflectors. (chimney & dome etc. omitted)

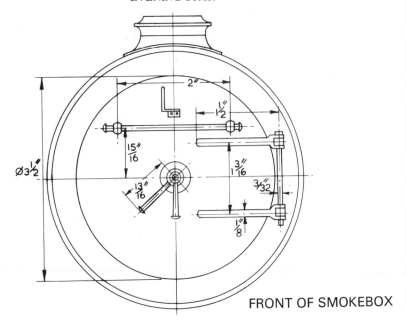

FRONT OF SMOKEBOX

size letter J). The outside is now turned to the profile shown, the hexagon middle part being hand filed while still in the lathe. In the absence of proper indexing gear, a reasonable hexagon can be produced by using the 3-jaw chuck, the centres of the jaws and the three key holes providing the necessary six positions.

The plungers or valves are turned from stainless steel. The 3/32 in. dia. stem is turned first, using 3/16 in. dia. stock, then holding them by the stems, turn 1/8 in. length an easy fit in the 5/32 in. hole in the bottom of the body and chamfer the shoulder at 45 deg. for 1/16 in. The "wings" at the extreme end can be milled. To do this, we need something to hold these valves firmly, so take a piece of mild steel about 5/16 in. diameter and drill this 3/32 in. diameter long enough to take the full length of the 3/32 in. dia. part of the valve. Then drill and tap 4 BA at right angles to take a brass clamping screw. Our holder can now be clamped under the lathe toolholder at centre height less 1/8 in. If a 3/16 in. dia. end mill is now used (in the 3-jaw or collet) and the holder turned through 120 deg. each time, nice "wings" will be left in the valve.

The safety valve springs can be 22 swg, tinned steel or stainless steel.

One of the biggest problems with *Evening Star* is to find room for the manifold or turret, on the top of the firebox. If made to scale, there will be only a shade over 3/16 in. between the top of the firebox and the underside of the cab roof, nowhere near enough to accommodate a manifold of the usual type. However, we can make up a fitting from brass or gunmetal of a section about 5/16 in. × ¼ in. and silversolder this to a short piece of 3/8 in. dia. stock, the latter being turned down and threaded 5/16 in. × 32t. to suit the bush on the top of the firebox. The fitting is then drilled a tight fit for a length of 3/16 in.

diameter thin-walled copper tube, and cross-drilled from the underside about No. 16 drill size to meet it. The main body of the manifold, incorporating four unions, all threaded $\frac{1}{4}$ in. × 40t. is then silversoldered on the end of the copper tube, which is itself silversoldered into the first fitting. The four branches serve respectively the injector steam valve, the blower, the whistle valve and the steam brake valve. The steam way through the union for the injector should be drilled as large as possible, at least 1/8 in. diameter, to give the injector "every chance", but the other three valves will function perfectly well with a smaller steam way, say 3/32 in. dia.

The length of the copper tube should be long enough to keep the main part of the manifold clear of the backhead. It will have to be bent downwards, as shown in my drawing, to clear the cab roof. It will immediately be asked how it is proposed to screw the completed fitting home, as it would foul the top of the firebox. The solution is to start with the tube etc. bent upwards sufficiently to clear the firebox while the fitting is screwed home. Then it can be bent downward as required, as the copper tube will be soft after the silversoldering operations. It is true of course that if the manifold has to be unscrewed again for any reason, this tube will have to be bent upwards again before doing so. But I don't think the second bending will harden the tube so much that it will kink or break off.

As the whistle valve could not be incorporated in the manifold, it is necessary to place it on one side of the firebox. I have therefore shown it on the left-hand side to the left of the regulator handle. The two unions on the right-hand side of the manifold are for the injector steam and blower, while the pipe for the whistle is taken from the left-hand side of the manifold.

I might mention here that there is no need for a third check valve (say in the lower part of the backhead), as the pipe from the usual tender hand pump can be connected up to that from the axle-driven pump, an extra non-return valve being arranged at the point of connection.

One of my problems was how to attach the running boards to the boiler. LBSC did not usually specify any form of lagging and cleading for his boilers, and in this case, the smokebox and boiler barrel specified were already very slightly over the strict scale diameter, so to add lagging and cleading was quite out of the question; the appearance would have been completely spoilt. So if the running boards (and the cab!) were to be attached to the boiler, it would have meant drilling and tapping the boiler barrel in quite a few places, and this is not a practice I would recommend.

The alternative is of course to attach these parts to the engine frames, as in most normal British locomotive types. But on *Evening Star*, the running boards are a long way above the top edge of the frames, and even the cab is some distance above. However, after much thought, I evolved two fairly simple brackets, built up from mild steel 3/16 in. and 1/8 in. thick, which can be bolted direct to the frames. The shorter one is located near the front, at the point where the running boards start to slope down to the buffer beam; the longer one is located at a point $\frac{3}{4}$ in. to the rear of the point where the top edge of the frame drops down by 3/8 in. between the leading coupled wheel and the second coupled wheel. These brackets can be bolted to the frames by 8 BA hexagon-head screws, and I don't think they will look too obtrusive.

At the extreme front end, the running boards are supported by the buffer beams, and at their rear end, they merge into the cab. The cab support gave me another headache! The boiler is, as usual, supported at the front end by the smokebox and saddle. At the rear end, it is usual to provide some form of expansion angle or bracket, to allow for the expansion of the boiler as it warms up. Where the boiler is of the narrow type, going down between the frames, it is quite easy to arrange for a sound rear fixing, but with a wide firebox type of boiler, lying above a narrow pair of frames, one is rather up against it.

Having attached the running boards rigidly to the front buffer beam, and having attached the cab sides rigidly to the running boards, it seemed to me that

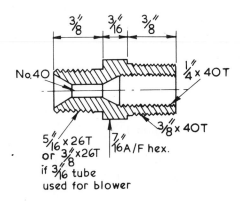

BLOWER UNION: for smokebox
(X2)   tubeplate.

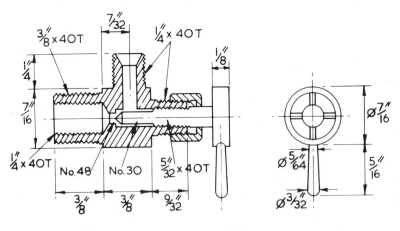

BLOWER VALVE: body gunmetal: pin st.steel (X2)

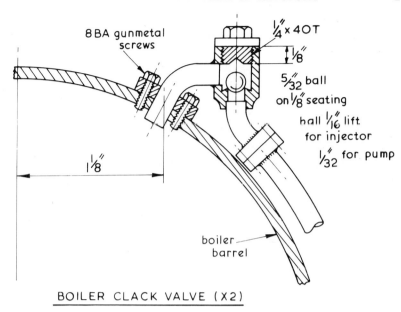

8 BA gunmetal screws

$\frac{1}{4}$" × 40 T

$\frac{1}{8}$"

$\frac{5}{32}$" ball on $\frac{1}{8}$" seating

ball $\frac{1}{16}$" lift for injector

$\frac{1}{32}$" for pump

$1\frac{1}{8}$"

boiler barrel

BOILER CLACK VALVE (X 2)

the best solution was to attach the cab rigidly to the frames, and allow the boiler, or rather the firebox, to slide through the cab spectacle plate as it expands. The movement is in any case very slight; it will probably be argued that the very first time the boiler is steamed, the paint around the join between the firebox and the spectacle plate will chip! But I don't think this is a very good argument; if the spectacle plate is matched very carefully to the shape of the firebox, but leaving 5 thou or so between the two, all the way round, this should be enough to avoid the paint being damaged, and in any case the problem is no worse than in a conventional model locomotive, where the boiler is allowed to slide and where the cab sides are bolted down rigidly to a rigid running board and footplate.

To hold the cab down, therefore, special brackets are suggested, of a more or less channel section; these are built up from mild steel by brazing, or maybe one of our castings suppliers will provide a gunmetal casting. This channel piece is then bolted firmly down to a short piece of 1 in. × 5/8 in. × 1/8 in. steel angle. A single 4 BA screw will be strong enough, one on each side of the locomotive. This could be hexagon-head, or better still, a socket cap screw. (Page 194.)

Another problem that arose was over the ashpan. The original overall height of the boiler, measured from the outside of the firebox wrapper down to the front bottom corner of the throatplate amounted to 5 & 31/32 in. But this would have meant that there was no room at all for the ashpan where this lies outside the frames. (The overall width of the bottom of the firebox being 5 & 3/16 in., while the width over the frame is only 3 & 1/8).

I have therefore had to reduce this overall height by 1/8 in.

The ashpan has to be "stepped", so as to obtain a reasonable depth between the frames, it was impossible to design it so that it could either be dropped straight down or withdrawn to the rear. It seemed to me therefore that it had best be made a permanent fixture retained by the weight of the firebox above it, which presses it firmly down against a simple sheet metal cover plate arranged over the trailing horns. This cover plate serves another important purpose—keeping the ashes out of the trailing axleboxes. The ashpan is however furnished with two hinged doors, which can be dropped to deposit ashes without their fouling the trailing axle. These are kept closed by a length of 1/8 in. dia. stainless steel which slides through guides as shown. A hole about $\frac{1}{4}$ in. diameter should be drilled in the drag beam just above the engine-tender coupling slot, and slightly to one side (either side will do). This rod could protrude through this hole by about $\frac{1}{4}$ in.—long enough to take a small knob, but not so long that it fouls the tender drag beam when right "home". To open the ashpan doors, the tender must of course be uncoupled, when the rod can be pulled until both doors drop open. A further small point—to allow the rod to pass between the bottom of the ashpan and the cover plate over the horns, a small central depression must be made in the top of the cover plate, as shown in the end elevation.

Reverting to the cab, the shape of the cab fitted to *Evening Star* is extraordinarily difficult to draw on the board, let alone make! This is because the sides slope upwards and inwards from the bottom line of the side windows, and slope inwards once again, at a steeper angle towards the roof, where it joins the main radius at the top ($4\frac{3}{4}$ in. radius at $\frac{3}{4}$ in. scale). To add to our difficulties, the sides and roof are flush all the way round, and the front or spectacle plate is made up of a short vertical piece above the level of the lookout windows (spectacles),

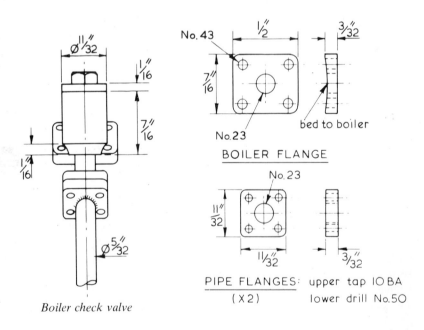

Boiler check valve

No. 43

bed to boiler

No. 23

BOILER FLANGE

No. 23

PIPE FLANGES: upper tap 10 BA
(X 2)   lower drill No. 50

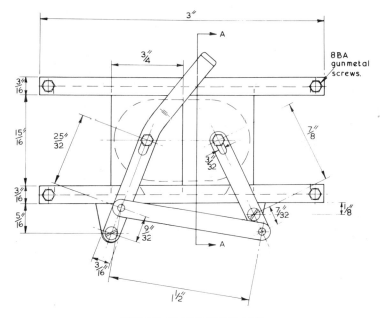

DETAILS OF FIRE DOOR (X2)

while the lower part of the spectacle plate not only slopes upwards and forwards, but slopes inwards and forwards when viewed in plan!! Well, it never rains but it pours, but I think the only way to tackle the cab is to take LBSC's own advice and make up paper or cardboard templates. In fact it might be worth while making up a complete cab in thin cardboard, using any quick-drying glue, then cutting this apart again, to make the metal pieces. I would suggest 18 s.w.g. hard brass for all the cab parts, except the floor, which might be 3/32 in. mild steel, as this has to carry the brackets holding the cab down to the frames, and don't forget that the cab, via the spectacle plate, holds the boiler down too!

Incidentally, the running boards could be made from $\frac{1}{2}$ in. brass angle, except for the sloping front part, where two lengths of 1/16 in. brass sheet will be required, the footsteps being inserted between the two. At the rear end, the angle can be flush-jointed to an extension of the cab side; a break is made here on the full-size locomotive.

One of the problems met when designing a wide firebox locomotive boiler is how to provide a fire-grate that can be removed easily for cleaning or renewal. Most wide firebox boilers are found on locomotives of the 4-6-2 wheel arrangement, or at least on locomotives having two or more trailing wheels underneath the firebox. *Evening Star*, however, is an exception to this, as here we have a wide firebox boiler placed on narrow type frames, and this makes it difficult to arrange for a convenient ashpan and grate.

Perhaps the best way is to make the grate in two halves, with the division down the longitudinal centre-line. In our case, this means that each half will be about 2¼ in. wide, narrow enough to pass through the narrower part of the ashpan (2 & 5/8 in. wide).

Before we can start on the tender for *Evening Star*, there are a few final details of the engine to be dealt with. First, the fire-door. This is of the sliding type, and is a fairly close copy of the full-size version, though inevitably somewhat out of scale, due to the larger firehole we require on a ¾ in. scale model.

The runners are made from 3/16 in. square brass; this is first reduced to 3/16 in. × 5/32 in., by milling or filing, then it is grooved 1/16 in. wide to a depth of 3/32 in. Note that the grooves should not extend quite to the ends of the runners, so as not to break into the fixing holes. Note also that one side of the channel so formed in the lower runner is removed for the length of the firehole, so that ashes will not collect here and foul the doors. 8 BA screws are used to bolt the runners to the boiler backhead, and they should preferably be of gunmetal or phos/bronze.

The doors are from 1/16 in. sheet metal. Mild steel, brass or stainless steel are all suitable, but the last mentioned is certainly to be preferred if builders are fortunate enough to have some of the right thickness. Make sure that the doors slide easily in their runners. The two extensions which carry the pivot pins for the door levers are best made of brass and silversoldered to the lower runner before this is bolted to the backhead.

The three levers are quite straightforward and can also be in any of the three metals mentioned above.

I need hardly say anything about the blower valve, as this is as described for most locomotives of 3½ in. or 5 in. gauge. It is threaded 3/8 in. × 40t. externally and ¼ in. × 40t. internally, to suit the hollow blower stay. At the smokebox end, the usual union fitting is used, but it might be a good plan to forsake the usual 40 thread here, for the attachment of the blower pipe, and use one 5/16 in. × 26t. or if the builder is using a 3/16 in. dia. pipe, for the twin blower required for the double chimney, the thread could be 3/8 in. × 26t. The coarser thread will be found easier to deal with in the confined space in the smokebox, especially as in this locomotive the smokebox tubeplate is situated rather a long way from the door!

The check or clack valves are somewhat different to the usual type, as they bolt on to the outside of the barrel, by means of a rectangular flange and four hex-head screws—again gunmetal if possible. Care should be taken to shape the flange to a good fit against the barrel, and a Hallite or Walkerite gasket will be required to ensure steam-tightness. The feed pipes are fitted by further flanges held together by four 10 BA screws.

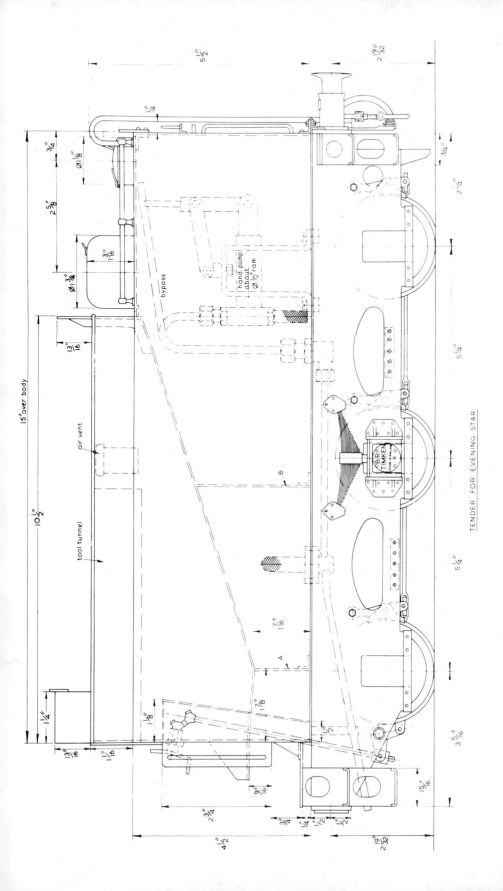

TENDER FOR EVENING STAR

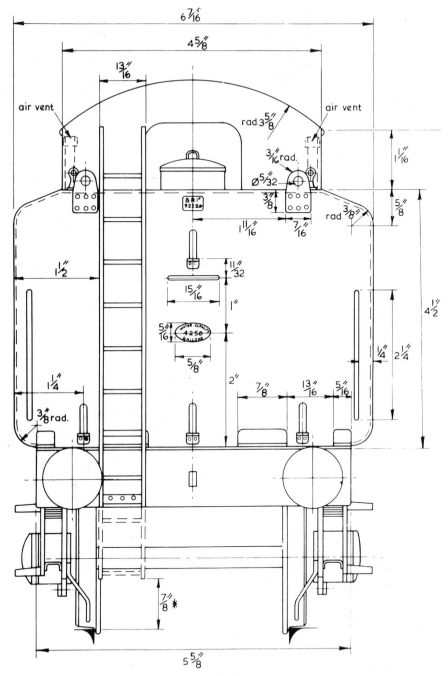

air vent

air vent

rad. 3⅝″

3/16″ rad.

Ø 5/32″

B.R.1″
92122e

WATER CAPACITY
4250
GALLONS

rad. ⅜″

3/16″ rad.

REAR END OF TENDER

✳ on some tenders ladder ends at base of body.

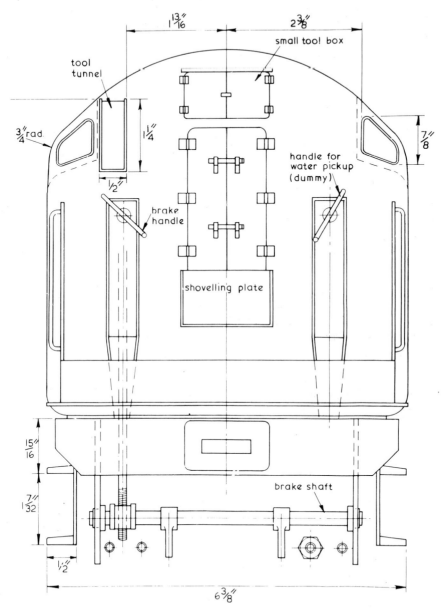

tool tunnel

small tool box

3/4″ rad.

1 13/16″

2 3/8″

1 1/4″

7/8″

1/2″

handle for water pickup (dummy)

brake handle

shovelling plate

15/16″

1 7/32″

brake shaft

1/2″

6 3/8″

FRONT END OF TENDER

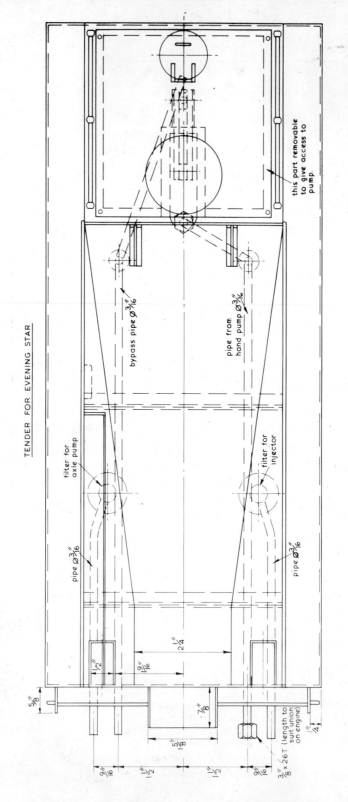

TENDER FOR EVENING STAR

PLAN OF TENDER BODY

(steps omitted)

this part removable to give access to pump.

bypass pipe Ø³⁄₁₆"

pipe from hand pump Ø³⁄₁₆"

filter for axle pump

filter for injector

pipe Ø³⁄₁₆"

pipe Ø³⁄₁₆"

³⁄₈" x 26T (length to suit union on engine)

2¼"

9⁄₁₆"

½"

5⁄₈"

7⁄₈"

¼"

5⁄₈"

9⁄₁₆"

1½"

1½"

9⁄₁₆"

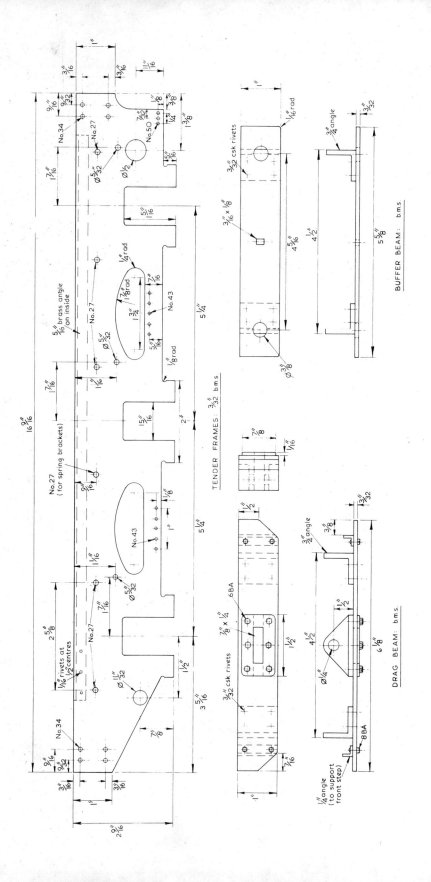

TENDER FRAMES: $\frac{3}{32}''$ b.m.s

BUFFER BEAM: b.m.s.

DRAG BEAM: b.m.s.

CHAPTER FOURTEEN

The tender

The tenders fitted to the British Railways standard locomotives were very different to any of those built by the pre-nationalised railways. Unfortunately for us, they are rather more difficult to build. This is mainly because instead of the usual flat floor or baseplate, the tank is built up with radiused corners, and the coal bunker is a sort of hopper made separately and fitted into the water tank, projecting well above it. The fireman's shovelling plate extends well forward into the engine cab, so as to enable the fireman to keep well clear of the gap between the engine and the tender, there being no "fall-plate".

The brake handle is mounted horizontally, with the screw spindle sloping slightly, so that the brake cross-shaft can be arranged well clear of the front wheels. However, on our model we can make a small modification to the brake

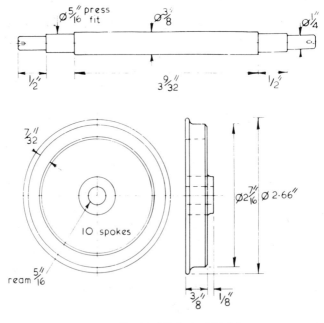

TENDER WHEELS & AXLES

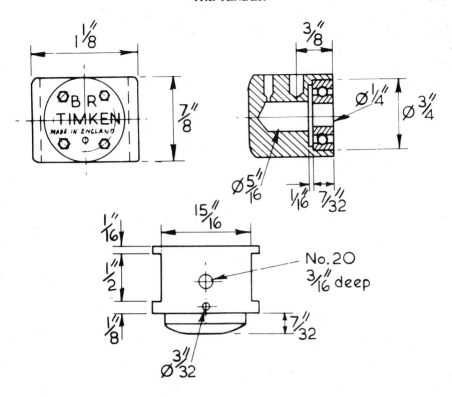

AXLEBOXES: G.M. ball bearing—light press fit

handle, putting it at a slight angle to the horizontal, and at 90 deg. to the spindle, so that we can use a standard pair of bevel wheels as supplied for the cab reverser. The difference will be hardly noticeable.

My drawings show the general arrangement of the tender, and also detail drawings of the frames, wheels, axles and axleboxes. However, it may not be a bad plan to make a start on the body and fit this to the chassis later on. Incidentally, in my G.A., I have drawn the Timken type axleboxes to exact scale, but those available from the Trade similar to the *Britannia* type will be a little wider and my detail drawing shows the Trade type. This became necessary owing to the ball races being somewhat out of scale on the diameter, no proper taper roller bearings being available in this size, as far as I know.

The tender body is made from 18 SWG sheet brass (1.2 mm.). The base is a separate piece, the radiused bottom edges of the sides being riveted or welded (in the full-size tender) on top of the base. This is most fortunate for us as it means that we do not have to bend the base and sides all in one piece. In LBSC's description of his *Britannia* tender, he seemed to be under the impression that the sides and base were in one piece in the prototype tender, and suggested that in the model, a break could be made along the middle of the bottom. But this is not so, as the official drawings show the construction clearly.

The sides could be riveted and soft soldered to the base, as the overlap "in the flat" is a good $\frac{1}{4}$ in. In my drawing, it is impossible to see this overlap as it is exactly hidden by the angle bolting the body to the buffer beam.

The back of the tender body can be fitted to the sides in the usual way, by brass angle $\frac{1}{4}$ in. or 5/16 in., a few copper rivets, countersunk and filed flush and the whole soft soldered to make the tank water-tight.

The sloping coal plate will need some support in the middle, so two "bulk-heads" are shown. The one I have marked A must be solid and soft soldered all around, as it forms the front of the water space, but the bulkhead marked B will require several holes drilled in it, near the bottom, to allow the water to reach the front of the tank. Three or four of 3/8 in. diameter should suffice, and this bulkhead will help to prevent surging if an emergency stop has to be made!

I have shown the usual hand pump, and this is set rather higher than usual so as to reduce the stroke of the handle to reasonable proportions. Even so, it will be necessary to cut quite a long slot in the top deck. However, I think a much better way is to make the whole of the top deck, complete with the water pickup dome and water filler, removeable, apart from a "border" of $\frac{1}{4}$ in. brass angle, which is required to support it. It may be argued that the ladder will prevent this top deck from lifting, but we could get over this by ending the extreme end of the ladder a short distance from the deck, securing it by an additional bracket (not shown in the drawing) riveted to the top edge of the back of the tender.

Incidentally, as tender hand pumps are really only provided for emergency use (as injectors are more reliable nowadays), perhaps it would be sensible not to screw this top deck down at all, but to rely on dowels of some kind or spring clips to hold it in place, so that it can be lifted off immediately the pump is required. Needless to say, a good deep filter should be let into the water filler, again easily removeable.

On the top of the coal bunker, we have (on the right-hand side only) what was officially described as the tool tunnel. This was presumably for the shovel and prickers etc. The recesses for the brake spindle, bearing and gears may

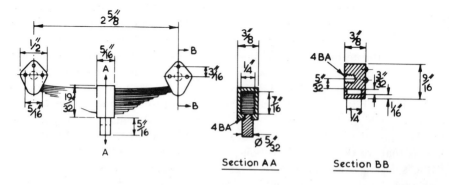

Section AA   Section BB

DETAILS OF TENDER SPRINGS

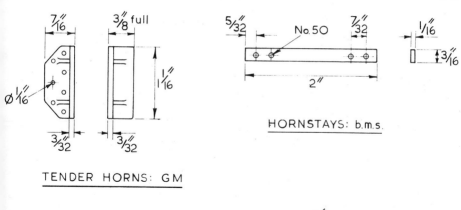

HORNSTAYS: b.m.s.

TENDER HORNS: GM

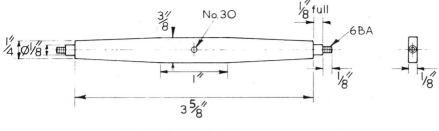

BRAKE BEAMS: b.m.s.

present a bit of a problem. The best way to deal with this, and for the similar arrangement on the left-hand side, where the (dummy) handle and spindle for the water pickup gear is situated, is to make the whole affair as a separate unit, then cut a slot in the tender front plate to receive it, measuring "on the job." A separate drawing of the brake arrangement is included, which should make matters clear.

The tender frames for *Evening Star*, as for LBSC's *Britannia*, are cut from 3/32 in. b.m.s. They are kept at the required distance apart by two simple frame stretchers, which will probably be obtainable from castings suppliers as gun-metal castings. Alternatively, 1/16 in. flat b.m.s. with ¼ in. brass angle flush riveted would be strong enough. The only reason why the flanges of these stretchers are turned upwards at the front and downwards at the rear is that they were arranged this way on the original tender to allow clearance for the water pickup gear.

To hold the tender body down on the frames, a length of 5/16 in. brass angle is used. This could be held to the frames by a row of 1/16 in. copper rivets, and to hold the angle to the tender body four or five 4 BA brass cheesehead screws on each side should be sufficient, but these should be put through thickening pieces on the upper side of the floor, the tapped holes being blind, as most of these screws would otherwise be running into the water space.

The buffer and drag beams are cut from 1 in. × 3/32 in. b.m.s., which is nearer to scale size than the more usual 1/8 in. thick material. ¾ in. × ¾ in. angle is

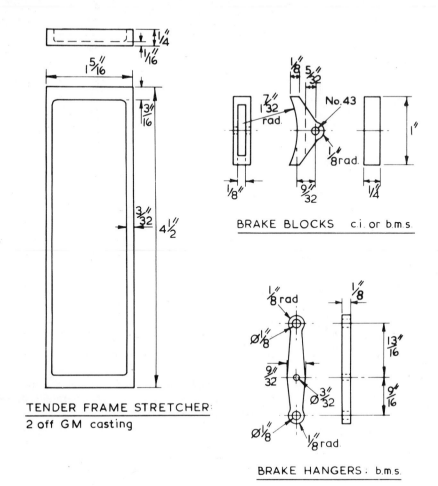

TENDER FRAME STRETCHER:
2 off GM casting

BRAKE BLOCKS   c.i. or b.m.s.

BRAKE HANGERS : b.m.s.

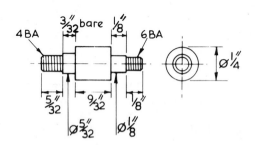

PIVOT PINS for BRAKE HANGERS 6 off b.m.s.

(X 2)

then used to fix the beams to the frames. But before assembling the frames, the bushes for the brake shaft should be turned up and pressed home, and the horns machined and fitted. The horns, gunmetal castings again, can be machined in the lathe, using the four-jaw, if no milling machine is available, as it is hardly worth while setting up the vertical-slide and machine vice just for this. The horns are held to the frames by seven 1/16 in. copper snaphead rivets each, and to ensure that they are correctly spaced, I find a good dodge is to insert between each pair a length of steel bar, previously machined to exactly 15/16 in. wide, plus a strip of thick paper, and clamp the whole up tightly with a toolmaker's clamp, laying the assembly against the frames, using the steel bar to locate it in the frames. The addition of the paper strip gives a nice working clearance, provided of course that the axleboxes are machined to correct size.

The axleboxes represent the full-size Timken taper roller bearing type, but actually use standard ¼ in. bore, ¾ in. O/D. ball bearings, and are the same as supplied for LBSC's *Britannia*. Machining them should not prove difficult; the sides and flanges are probably best done first, using our usual vertical-slide cum machine vice cum end-mill technique. They are held in the four jaw, using strips of brass 3/32 in. thick inserted between the flanges, and set to run as truly as possible. They are then drilled 5/16 in. diameter and bored out to take the ball bearings. This is where the Martin Cleeve "swing-clear" boring toolholder comes into its own, enabling one to swing the tool out of the way while a ball race is tried for size. For beginner's benefit, the ball races should not be made a press fit, but a tight push fit, just tight enough to ensure that they will not work out again in service.

The wheels and axles should be straightforward turning jobs and no problem to those who have successfully completed the driving and coupled wheels and

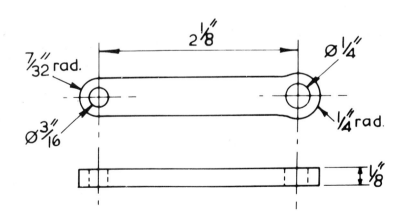

ENGINE TENDER COUPLING

b.m. s.

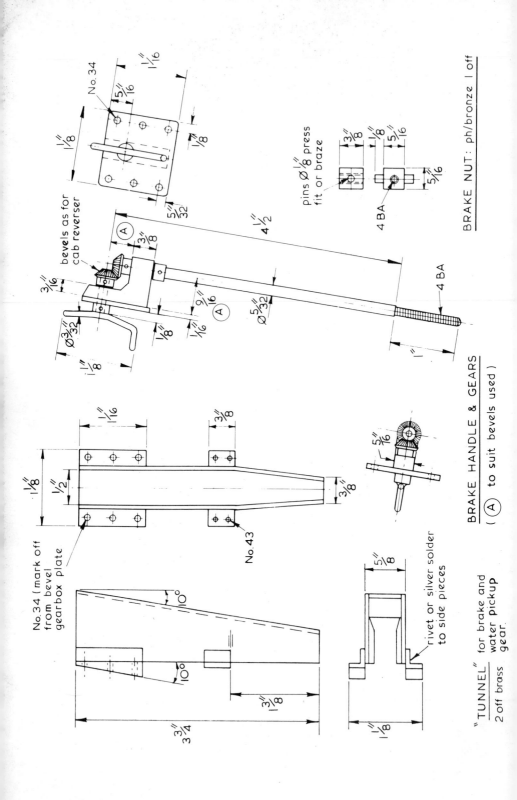

No. 34

1 1/16

5/16

1/8

1/8

5/32

bevels as for cab reverser

3/16

Ø 3/32

1/8

1/16

9/16

A

A

3/8

Ø 5/32

4 1/2

4 BA

1"

4 BA

pins Ø 1/8 press fit or braze

3/8

1/8

5/16

5/16

4 BA

BRAKE NUT: ph/bronze 1 off

BRAKE HANDLE & GEARS

(A) to suit bevels used)

5/16

No. 34 (mark off from bevel gearbox plate

1 1/8

1/16

3/8

1/2

3/8

No. 43

10°

10°

3/8

3 3/4
3"

5/8

1/8

rivet or silver solder to side pieces

"TUNNEL" for brake and water pickup gear.
2 off brass

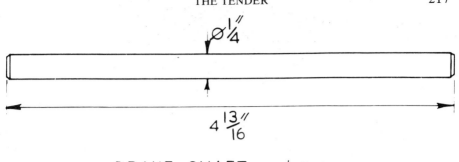

BRAKE SHAFT :   b.m.s.

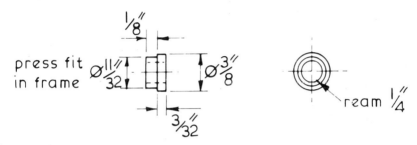

BUSHES for BRAKE SHAFT: 2 off GM

the pony truck wheels. The wheels, incidentally, have been dimensioned to the new ME/SMEE standards.

Although castings will be available for the tender springs, many builders may prefer proper laminated built-up springs. Although metal spring leaves could be used, a great deal would have to be cut out to make them light enough for a tender, unless the whole spring was made very much thinner than scale, but that would defeat the whole object, so much the best solution is to use heat-treated tufnol. Tufnol strips 1/32 in. thick and ½ in. wide can be obtained ready cut and these could be cut in half. Alternatively 3/8 in. strip could be used, the hangers etc. being made wider to suit. The full number of spring leaves can be used, the three top ones being made the full length (2.7/8 in.) and inserted in the slots of the hangers.

The hangers are held to the tender frames by 4 BA bolts, inserted from the back, into tapped holes in the hangers. If these are screwed in tightly the hangers should not be liable to rotate, but a small pin about 1/16 in. dia. could be put in from the back if desired, which would eliminate this possibility. The spring leaves are clamped together in the middle by the fitting that we might call the centre-buckle, this being made from mild steel of 3/8 in. × 5/16 in. sections, with a slot deep enough to take the 14 spring leaves. The leaves are then clamped by the 4 BA threaded pin which also acts as a register into the No. 20 recess in the top of the axlebox. This No. 20 blind hole, by the way, should be positioned from the pin in the spring buckle after the springs and hangers have been fitted to the frames, as its position will of course depend on whether ¼ in. or 3/8 in. wide spring leaves have been used.

Brake Gear

I have made a slight rearrangement of the tender brake standard to enable the standard bevel gears, as used for the cab reverser, to be used again. Starting with the "tunnel", this is made up from brass sheet, the joints being silver soldered. It is of rather awkward shape, and it is best to complete it and finish the cutaway in the tender front plate to suit, rather than tackling the matter in the reverse order. To hold the three sides of the "tunnel" together for silver soldering, soft iron wire can be twisted around it, at each end, and only a very light touch of Easyflo used, to avoid soldering the wire as well. The "tunnel" is bolted to the tender front plate by four 8 BA bolts through the small angles fitted near the bottom, and by six 6 BA bolts put through the top angles, but the latter should not be fitted yet, as these six screws have to be put through the bevel gear bearing first.

The bevel gear bearing is cut from a slab of brass 5/16 in. thick, although our castings people may provide a suitable gunmetal casting. In either case, it can be silversoldered to the nearly-square fixing plate, which is 1.1/8 in. × 1.1/16

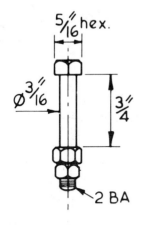

ENGINE COUPLING

PIN (permanent)

b.m.s.

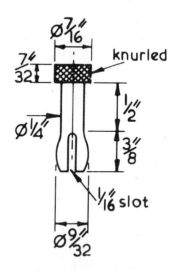

TENDER COUPLING

PIN (removable)

b.m.s.

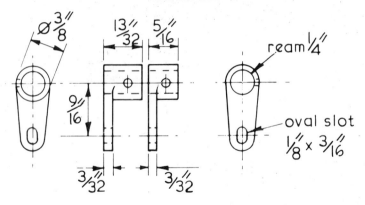

LEVERS for BRAKE NUT (I pair) b.m.s.

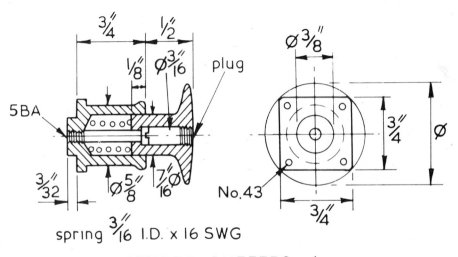

TENDER BUFFERS : b.m.s.

in. and 1/16 in. thick. The brake handle is made from 3/32 in. dia. mild or silver steel, bent to shape and silversoldered to a 1/8 in. long collar, $\frac{1}{4}$ in. diameter. The collar is then pinned to the short 1/8 in. dia. shaft carrying one of the bevels. The vertical shaft, carrying the other bevel, is 5/32 in. dia. silver steel, turned down to 1/8 in. dia. at the top and to 0.142 in. dia. at the bottom, for threading 4 BA.

The brake cross shaft is $\frac{1}{4}$ in. dia. and this carries the levers, three in all, the pair which engage with the brake nut being slotted as shown, to allow for the angularity as the nut is raised and lowered.

Three brake beams are required, all identical, and cut from 3/8 in. × 1/8 in. b.m.s. Single central pull rods are used, again 1/8 in. diameter, and a coupling with left and right-hand threads is used between the cross shaft and the first

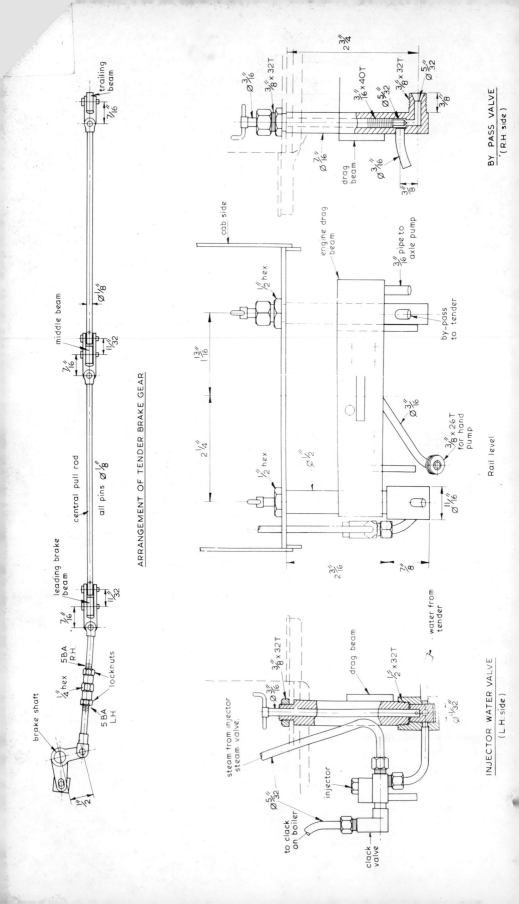

ARRANGEMENT OF TENDER BRAKE GEAR

trailing beam

$\frac{7}{16}''$

middle beam

$\frac{7}{16}''$ $\frac{11}{32}''$

$\varnothing \frac{1}{8}''$

central pull rod

all pins $\varnothing \frac{1}{8}''$

leading brake beam

$\frac{7}{16}''$ $\frac{11}{32}''$

$\frac{1}{4}''$ hex   5 BA R.H.

locknuts

5 BA L.H.

brake shaft

$\frac{1}{2}''$

BY PASS VALVE
(R.H side)

$2\frac{3}{4}''$

$\varnothing \frac{3}{16}''$

$\frac{3}{8}'' \times 32T$

$\frac{3}{16}'' \times 4OT$

$\varnothing \frac{5}{32}''$

$\frac{3}{8}'' \times 32T$

$\varnothing \frac{5}{32}''$

$\frac{3}{8}''$

$\varnothing \frac{1}{16}''$

drag beam

$\varnothing \frac{3}{16}''$

$\frac{3}{8}''$

cab side

$\frac{1}{2}''$ hex

$1\frac{13}{16}''$

$2\frac{1}{4}''$

$\frac{1}{2}''$ hex

$\varnothing \frac{1}{2}''$

engine drag beam

$\frac{3}{16}''$ pipe to axle pump

by-pass to tender

$\varnothing \frac{3}{16}''$

$\frac{3}{8}'' \times 26T$ for hand pump

$\varnothing \frac{11}{16}''$

$2\frac{3}{16}''$

$\frac{7}{8}''$

Rail level

INJECTOR WATER VALVE
(L.H. side)

$\frac{3}{8}'' \times 32T$

$\varnothing \frac{3}{16}''$

steam from injector steam valve.

drag beam

$\frac{1}{2}'' \times 32T$

water from tender

$\varnothing 1\frac{1}{2}''$

$\varnothing \frac{5}{32}''$

injector

to clack on boiler

clack valve

brake beam, for adjustment purposes. The remaining items of the brake gear—the hangers, blocks and hanger pivot pins are all quite straightforward and require no description.

Now we come to the tender buffers, with the old problem that the frames, being $4\frac{1}{2}$ in. apart, are in the way of any kind of spindle projecting through the buffer beams. However, as the buffer stocks have square bases, there should be no difficulty. The stocks are turned from $\frac{3}{4}$ in. square mild steel, with a short projection of 3/8 in. dia. to locate them in the holes previously drilled in the buffer beam. The heads are turned next, from 1 in. dia. mild steel, after which the stocks are drilled and bored a good fit for the heads. A special bolt, with a short 5 BA thread, is used to prevent the head from coming out, and after assembly, the clearance hole in the head is plugged tightly, and any excess filed flush. The spring is 3/16 in. I.D. and of 16 SWG. A fairly strong spring is desirable in a tender buffer.

Returning now to the engine, we require an injector water valve and a bypass valve for the axle-driven feed pump. These are both bolted to the 3/32 in. thick cab floor, the former being on the left just clear of the drag beam, in fact it may be fitted hard up against the inside of the beam which will give it further support. It is of the full bore type. If the short pipe from the water valve to the injector is silversoldered to the body of the valve, the injector itself will require no other fixing, being supported by its pipes. *IMPORTANT*. As in this design, both the injector water valve and the bypass valve are fitted on the engine rather than on the tender, the water in the tender will run out if the tender is disconnected from the engine at any time, unless of course additional taps or cocks are fitted in the tender pipes. But I don't think this is any disadvantage in practice, as the rubber tube normally used to connect engine pipes to tender pipes can be closed temporarily be a simple spring clip whenever the tender is disconnected from the engine, and I don't really think that additional cocks are justified. At least it will be an easy job draining the tender at the end of the day's running without having to turn it upside down!

A final detail—the engine-tender coupling. This is made from $\frac{1}{2}$ in. × 1/8 in. b.m.s. and is permanently attached to the engine with the bolt shown. The tender coupling pin is made with a large knurled head and is slotted out as shown, so that it can be "sprung" into position.

This completes my description of *Evening Star*, so it only remains for me to wish builders of this fine locomotive every success in their efforts, and good steaming on the track.

Index